OPERATION
MORNING LIGHT

OPERATION MORNING LIGHT

Terror in Our Skies
The True Story of Cosmos 954

Leo Heaps

**PADDINGTON
PRESS LTD**
NEW YORK & LONDON

This book is dedicated to the memory of A.A. Heaps, who set the example.

Library of Congress Cataloging in Publication Data

Heaps, Leo.
  Operation Morning Light.

  Includes index.
  1. Artificial satellites, Russian – Accidents.
I. Title.
TL796.5.R9C674   629.43'4'09047   78-16614
ISBN 0 7092 0323 3
ISBN 0 448 22425 9 (US and Canada only)

Filmset in England by SX Composing, Rayleigh, Essex.
Printed and bound in the United States.
Designed by Sandra Shafee
Cover photograph by Horst Munzig,
courtesy of Susan Griggs Agency.

IN THE UNITED STATES
PADDINGTON PRESS
Distributed by
GROSSET & DUNLAP

IN THE UNITED KINGDOM
PADDINGTON PRESS

IN CANADA
Distributed by
RANDOM HOUSE OF CANADA LTD.

IN SOUTHERN AFRICA
Distributed by
ERNEST STANTON (PUBLISHERS) (PTY) LTD

IN AUSTRALIA AND NEW ZEALAND
Distributed by
A.H. & A.W. REED

Contents

Acknowledgments

The research for this book took me to many places in the United States and Canada. In each place there were people who helped me in countless ways. I would like to be able to thank all of them properly, but this brief list (in no particular order of importance) will have to suffice.

In Yellowknife I received much useful advice and information from Sig Sigvaldason, owner and editor of the *Yellowknifer* newspaper. Lieutenant Colonel Bill Butchart provided many facilities as well as the exceptional experience of riding on a search flight in the wilderness. Through his kindness I met the men and women of the Northern Command, and gained considerable insight into the entire search organization.

At the Canadian Forces Base in Edmonton, Colonel David Garland spared me valuable time for long talks when he was deeply immersed in the arduous search for Cosmos. Richard Lynn and Dr. June Engel offered special advice in a number of ways, and I thank both of them.

In Washington, General Mahlon Gates painstakingly enlarged upon the role played by American personnel in recovering Cosmos debris.

In Las Vegas, Dave Jackson of the Department of Energy opened many doors; he arranged the talks I wanted to have with many key personnel from Lawrence Livermore Laboratory and elsewhere. At Lawrence Livermore I was passed into the capable hands of Jeffrey Garberson, who in turn introduced me to others from whom I picked up various threads of the fascinating story of the days before the crash of the satellite.

At the Geological Survey in Ottawa, Arthur Darnley directed me to people who had worked in Operation Morning

Light from the beginning. Friends at the Canadian Ministry of Mines, Energy and Resources made possible an important visit to the Whiteshell Nuclear Research Establishment at Pinawa. The Honorable Barnett Danson, Canadian Minister of Defense, took a personal interest in my activities and placed many facilities at my disposal.

Almost two dozen people sat patiently through long and exhausting interviews with me in circumstances far from comfortable. Without their generosity and forbearance this book would have been much more difficult to write. Some of them I have already named above; all are listed at the back of the book. To their names I must add those of Colonel Jean Boulet of Canadian Forces Public Affairs and Colonel Beverly Totman, Edmonton, who kept me constantly briefed with the daily fact sheets of Operation Morning Light.

My last and personally most important acknowledgment is to my wife Tamar. Many months of fatiguing travel kept me constantly away from home, and for her tolerant understanding I am truly grateful.

Prologue

Two days after the Soviet spy satellite Cosmos 954 splattered its debris across northern Canada, I decided to try to find the truth behind this disturbing incident. If I had misjudged the situation my journey would be nothing more than a curious trip into a land that had always excited my imagination. In that case I would forget the event. If, on the other hand, I discovered that the crash of the maverick satellite was really a major happening, a book would be written. However, I would have been happier if nothing of any importance had occurred, and there was no danger to wildlife or mankind. But this was not to be.

This book is proof that I was right. In the winter wilderness of the Barren Lands, the remote area of Canada's Northwest Territory where the satellite crashed to earth, I came across much more than I could have imagined. Not only would the event absorb my total interest but so would the people. Radioactive contamination was widespread. The story eventually took me from the Barrens to Santa Barbara, Las Vegas, Washington, Ottawa, Winnipeg. The trail was long and revealing. I talked with defense ministers, scientists, politicians and military men. I saw at work the entire US and Canadian nuclear search capability. I encountered politics and intrigue; silence where there should have been frankness; secrecy and official reticence.

Operation Morning Light, as the Canadians code-named the Cosmos operation, was the most massive search for nuclear debris ever undertaken. It was a foretaste of operation doomsday. But for the Canadians this was not an exercise. It was real. What had happened on a great expanse of territory in North America grew profoundly disturbing as I learned more with the passing of time and met people who spent long days attempting to clean up the fields of contamination. Unfortunately the story has no ending. For the end is in man himself as much as it is in Cosmos. I had never written a book with so much concentrated intensity. And while I felt at the beginning that time was of the essence, when I finished I knew I had been wrong. The story of Cosmos 954 is more like a story of our time. The morning light that burst over the Barren Lands of northern Canada that day in January, 1978, really burst upon the world.

Part One

PREPARATION

1

Cosmos 954 was dying in the infinite darkness of space. Its death vigil was being secretly kept by tracking stations around the world.

Cosmos had been shot into orbit by the Soviet Union from the Tyuratam launch site in Central Asia on September 18, 1977. The length of the object was reputed to be somewhere in the vicinity of fifty feet and the total weight probably over five tons. But these figures could only be surmised by the North American Air Defense (NORAD) sunk deep in the heart of the Rockies in Cheyenne, Colorado. Here technicians of the Space Defense Center gathered information from a number of vital tracking stations. On their radar screens they monitored over 4,485 orbiting satellites, each of which looked like a tiny speck of dust hurtling about in the limitless void. At NORAD, each speck – whether a functioning satellite or a piece of cosmic waste – is given a number by which it is known until its death. This particular satellite had been designated number 10361.

Cosmos 954 had distinct qualities that set it aside from other space objects. Some people said it was designed for ocean surveillance, to find and report on United States nuclear submarines and warships. Others suggested that it could manipulate the weather on earth. What puzzled many was its unusual power pack of 110 pounds of highly enriched uranium 235. No one knew for certain, but it was assumed that Cosmos' core was similar in design to a Soviet reactor known by the name Romashka. If this was the case, then the lead-encased uranium core would be about the size of a medium-sized watermelon. Its structure would consist of layers of fuel discs, a thermal insulator enclosed by two reflectors at either end through which ran two control rods. This in turn would be encased in a barrel-like structure covered by small rectangular fins of the converter radiator.

Cosmos 954 was designed to circle 150 miles above the earth, making an orbit exactly every eighty-eight minutes at a steady speed of 15,000 miles per hour. Its life span was supposedly unlimited.

But by December 15 Cosmos was tracing an irregular pattern on the consoles at NORAD. Captain David Tohlen, as chief orbital analyst, had watched the satellite since early November. Tohlen knows that, since the Russians launched the first Sputnik in 1957, over 6,000 objects have gone out of orbit. Most have soared off into outer space never to be heard of again. Others have crashed into the sea. Some have disintegrated into fragments and are still circling the earth, and many have simply vanished without a trace from the radar screens.

At times Cosmos seemed to hop through space, descending fifty miles or more, then bouncing back up from the atmosphere like a stone skipping along the surface of a pond. It was writhing and twisting, slowly exhausting itself, battling for survival as if its nuclear-powered engine had developed a leak. The malfunction affected the speed that Cosmos required to maintain course. An unpredictable fault had changed a manageable satellite into a runaway. But no one who watched it in the Western world understood its significance. Perhaps the Soviets had issued new commands which Cosmos refused to obey. Whatever the case, they offered no explanations and gave no help. They seemed to be waiting, but no one knew why.

A Canadian named Colonel Gerald Patterson, one of NORAD's so-called "Doomsday Troops," regarded the antics of Cosmos with unusual attention. His role in the joint Canada/ United States defense organization is to give immediate warning to Ottawa and Washington of an imminent nuclear attack on North America. In the event of such an attack, multiple warhead missiles and nuclear aircraft of the United States would retaliate within seconds. There were tense people in Colorado who must have been thinking of this possibility.

NORAD had unique, frightening powers. Its Commander could act on his own under certain circumstances. For instance, if communications with Washington broke down, he could set off the almost instantaneous nuclear response against Soviet attack. Cosmos carried no warhead, but the uranium core might be able to heat up to the point where it could explode.

Each successive eighty-eight minutes brought a new alteration in the course of the satellite. Coming up from the south, it veered steadily westward so that now on any one orbit it might streak high above Maui, Hawaii, where it had been visually reported in the night. On another orbit it would pass over Miami and Detroit.

Only a handful of chosen people in the military establishment and government knew about the crazily orbiting satellite. When pressed for information, the Russians said Cosmos had a fail-safe mechanism, and if it became absolutely uncontrollable it would automatically break into three parts. The part that contained the uranium power pack would be catapulted 900 miles further out into space, where it would orbit for a thousand years and eventually burn itself out, causing no hazard to human life on earth.

But a month after discovery Captain David Tohlen, chief orbital analyst, noticed that Cosmos had not broken up in space. In fact, it was very much in one piece, and it was causing concern to the United States Security Council. On a day-by-day basis, a team of twenty-eight computer analysts at NORAD did their best to figure out what was going to happen. With each orbit, the speed of Cosmos was diminishing – first by a tenth, then by two-tenths of a minute. At 15,000 miles an hour, a change in speed of a tenth of a minute makes a difference of 25 miles. The prognosis made by the scientists at the National Aeronautics Space Administration (NASA) stated there would be a reentry in April, when the last decaying orbits would send Cosmos crashing through the atmosphere. But there was still plenty of time for conjecture. The area of reentry could be predicted by men like Tohlen to within a distance of plus or minus 6,000 miles, the width of Canada. But all the ten major stations from which NORAD correlated information in different locations around the world would be of little precise assistance. The Tracking and Impact Prediction program that fell under the NORAD authority could only be approximate.

The 1971 agreement between the United States and the Soviet Union provided for an immediate exchange of information regarding unidentified space machines, since any unreported objects orbiting over either the North American continent or the Soviet Union could trigger off a sequence of flashpoint responses that might lead to a nuclear conflict. And while a decaying satellite would not, under normal detection procedures, be conceived as a hostile nuclear missile, that possibility could not be ruled out. The appropriate US authorities had to be notified by NORAD.

The computers calculated that the chances of Cosmos hitting a land mass were only one in twelve. Indeed, one computer even figured the possibility one in a million. A harmless landing in the ocean was the consensus.

In a matter of a few days, Captain Tohlen and his associates had analyzed 5,000 observations of Cosmos from tracking stations in all parts of the world except the Soviet Union. Telescopic cameras, advanced radar and classified watching devices were on emergency alert. Normally the computer printouts were compiled on a routine weekly basis. But for Cosmos 954 they were done daily and the results minutely scrutinized by the CIA. Signals were coming in regularly from the Maui sighting station in Hawaii, whose powerful telescopic camera could detect the reflected glow of a satellite at 20,000 miles. It would probably be among the first tracking stations to know when Cosmos took its final lunge earthward.

2

There were other people, with headquarters in California, who were competent to predict the general reentry path of Cosmos 954. These individuals, among them some of the best scientific minds in the nation, belong to a little-known American group called the Nuclear Emergency Search Team (NEST). They are trained to detect the precise areas of danger in a nuclear emergency and then proceed to neutralize the sources of radiation. NEST's members are spread mainly through the southwestern United States in the nuclear weapons-designing institutions controlled by the University of California and several other research laboratories under captive contracts to the United States Department of Energy. The group has its operational headquarters in the sun-baked valley of Las Vegas, less than 65 miles from the 1,350-square mile atomic test site at prefabricated Mercury City.

In twenty-five years over five hundred nuclear weapons tests have been conducted at the Nevada Test Site. It is in a long, wide hollow of land, ranged by mountain peaks that soar into the pure blue sky of the desert. Most of the year the peaks are snow-covered. At the mountain resorts one can ski on hot days while the tourists in town play tennis and golf, swim and gamble at the sumptuous hotels along the Las Vegas strip. The Test Site is part of the extended desert complex run by the Department of Energy, 850,000 acres of arid valleys, serrated gray sandy hills, dried-up lake beds that fill suddenly in the occasional flash floods. Some of the mountains rise to a height of almost 8,000 feet and when the winds whip down from the pinnacles they stir up formidable sand storms. Wind is an important factor on the site. It determines the safety of the tests in the event of leakage from the underground tunnels and bore holes where nuclear devices are detonated. Wind and weather have to be exactly right before the firing equipment is activated.

The Test Site has a well-equipped complex that includes a railway, airstrip, offices, dormitories, recreational facilities and laboratories. At the control point on the crest of Yucca Pass is Test Operations Room CP1, where scientists and technicians monitor, measure, and theorize about the effects of the great explosions. Their reports are evaluated at the scientific laboratories which design the devices.

Atmospheric testing stopped in 1971, and since then all the devices have been exploded below ground. In that time there have been eighteen instances where radioactivity has been accidentally released. "Small amounts" of radioactivity, it has been officially stated, were detected beyond the boundary of the Government-controlled area. The official report confirms that "these small releases have never exposed any member of the public to radiation doses exceeding the conservative levels established in authorized guides." However, doses are cumulative and often a decade or more might pass before their effects can be accurately determined. In 1957 a 44-kiloton bomb exploded from a tower at Yucca Flat, the present scene of tests on the site. This is about a fifth of the yield of present explosions. Two decades later, ten of the soldiers who were supposedly a safe distance from the site have come down with leukemia. Others who participated in the experiment have yet to be traced.

One of the bizarre anomalies of the Nevada testing can be seen inside the high-rise hotels along the Las Vegas Strip when a nuclear explosion takes place. Within the giant casinos, glittering with constellations of flashing lights, the gamblers hardly look up from their games of roulette and blackjack as buildings and tables tremble beneath them from the shock that rumbles out like an earthquake from the underground blast. The explosion vaporizes and melts large strata of rock below ground in the area of the detonation. This in turn causes subsidence, with the result that hundreds of acres of the desert test site have become pockmarked with shallow craters several hundred feet across. A moonscape has bloomed on the brown, sun-burned land of Yucca Flat, trapping beneath it a field of deadly nuclear radiation. The cold, artificial illumination of the Strip which lights up the night sky above Las Vegas is pallid compared to the brilliant flash that is born unseen below the desert. Two huge excesses live in harmony, side by side. But nothing in the gaudy shows of the Strip equals the extravaganza performed at Mercury City. And the men who run each city are as different as the events they control.

The experience derived from testing nuclear weapons in the Nevada desert has produced in NEST an organization designed to counter the radiation hazard. This organization is ready to go anywhere in the world. And it has both the men and the tools with which to do the job.

Operation Morning Light took place in northern Canada but it had more remote origins in the desert not far from the pleasure domes of the Las Vegas Strip.

3

The United States Department of Energy building on South Highland Avenue, Las Vegas, is officially designated as the Nevada Operations Office (NEVOO). It is a big, stolid, dull building about 300 feet long and two stories high, solidly built, finished in brown brick and white block. Finely trimmed lawns brighten the entrance. Freight hoists and a seven-foot-high fence strung with barbed wire enclose a paved rear yard guarded by armed officers. The security guards command the gates and all the loading facilities. There are few windows in the building and most of them are small, hermetically sealed, and on the second floor. On a tall mast, a US flag flutters over the entrance in the warm breeze. Below the US flag is another smaller one representing the DOE. Several small yellow plaques fixed on the entrance walls warn: "No trespassing. By Order of the U.S. Atomic Energy Commission." Across the street and beyond a railway track one can clearly see Caesar's Palace, the Flamingo and Circus Circus soaring over the Las Vegas Strip, thousands of twinkling lights ablaze in the bright daylight.

In the small foyer one becomes suddenly aware that this is an office unlike any other government office. The surroundings are both hostile and attractive. At the far end a stony-faced guard with thin lips and robot-like reflexes displays an open-holstered automatic. He stands behind a glass-encased booth. Studiously he checks and fingers the identity cards of everyone who passes, even those who leave briefly to go to the adjacent cafeteria or toilets. The guard acts as if he were interested only in the identity cards worn on the lapel, not in the faces. The cards have an extra thickness due to a layer of sensitive film on the back which measures radiation exposure.

Near the main door is a model of a Polynesian outrigger canoe. The model was given, it says, by the people of Enewetak Atoll to the DOE to thank them for trying to make their island habitable after testing in the atmosphere was concluded in the Marshall Islands. When the USA and USSR signed a treaty banning atmospheric tests, a giant cleanup began on Enewetak Atoll. It started over three years ago and still continues. The 250 islanders hope that one day the soil will reach the required safety standard and they will be able to return to Enewetak.

Since 1972 the Nevada Test Site has been run by an affable, retired Brigadier General named Mahlon E. Gates. Before coming to Las Vegas, Gates was at Redstone Arsenal, Alabama, where his duties were primarily concerned with what is known as the Safeguard Ballistic Missile System. Officially he is called Manager of the Test Site, but this hardly describes a man who employs 6,000 people and whose yearly budget is $10.4 billion. Indeed, Gates is the largest employer in the State of Nevada. Nor is Nevada his sole responsibility: his jurisdiction extends as far as Honolulu, to the Pacific Area Support Office, accountable for all testing of nuclear devices in that region. The Honolulu office is kept in a state of constant readiness should testing in the atmosphere be recommenced. This means facilities on the remote Johnston Island are on a standby basis. Gates controls a formidable team of scientists, technicians and auxiliary personnel. He reports to General Joseph Bratton in Washington and Bretton has means of reaching the President without delay.

Gates is a warm man, a soldier in civilian clothes, a man of quiet habits and low voice. He is used to command and obedience, and his judgments of people are quick and to the point. He speaks courteously and with calm authority. Perhaps no man in the United States has more to do with the overall testing mechanisms of nuclear military weapons than himself. The nuclear world in which he lives is an integral part of his life. He is thoroughly committed personally and publicly to weapons testing.

Out of 606 nuclear tests "announced" by the US government

as of January 1, 1978, 468 have been made at the Nevada Test Site. Now and then, because of the great explosive power of some of the warheads, experiments are conducted elsewhere. Three explosions have taken place in Amchitka, in the Aleutians, over the considerable protests of the Canadian government and especially the people of British Columbia. Gates has to live with the criticism and the power he wields. And he has found that the easiest way to do this is to surround himself with the kind of dedication which reflects his own committed attitude. This is the tone set for all the other employees of NEVOO and its captive institutions.

NEVOO is a neat, tidy world, a hard-working elite community where there are no hours and where everyone is on call day or night, ready to leave for any part of the world on immediate notice. It is not good here to have too much imagination, to speculate too long on anything but the work at hand. Too much imagination and speculation might have an adverse effect on the fine discipline that knits the organization together.

The contamination of the small Pacific atoll of Enewetak is typical of the problems that confront NEVOO. The team sent there to decontaminate found that radiation persisted in all forms of life, in water and air. As Gates explained to me, this presented formidable difficulties.

"We made our radiological hazards study and evaluation from November of 1972 to February of 1973 and put out a report," Gates said. "The DOE in Enewetak has the responsibility for establishing a radiological hazard and criteria for the island cleanup in order to support either living, agriculture or periodic visitation."

Gates went on to explain that the "cleanup has just started." The total population of 250 were removed when the atmospheric tests began in the late 1940s and early 1950s. After twenty-eight years, dangerous contamination still prevents the islanders from returning. Although full-scale efforts have been made to remove the radioactive fallout, the island is still declared a hazard for human life.

When I spoke with Gates, he also enlarged upon some of the

major functions of his department.

"There have been a number of aircraft accidents in which atomic weapons were involved. Two of the most important were in Palomares, Spain and Thule, Greenland. As a result of them we developed the Surveillance, Accident Nuclear Detection System (SANDS) capability. It involved a series of detectors that could locate gamma and neutron sources. There have been various threats in the United States, hoaxes some of them. About thirty threats in eight years."

The day of the homemade atomic bomb became a reality in 1977, when John Aristotle Phillips, a Princeton undergraduate, designed one as a project for his physics class. In the same year, *Mechanics Illustrated* published an article showing how it could be done. Gates knew about these things. And he was understandably nervous on the subject. All someone needed to build a nuclear weapon was a small quantity of enriched uranium 235, the same material Cosmos carried in its reactor.

"In November 1974, I was given a mission," Gates recalls, "to bring into focus all the assets of the DOE to provide a common logistic support system, a communications system and a rapid response so that we could go out any time there was a nuclear threat." The Nuclear Emergency Search Team, NEST, grew out of that mission. In 1977 the team had its first full-scale exercise, called NEST 77. "The team had to find and render safe a source of radiation. One of the recommendations we came up with was that we had to have a full-scale loading and flyaway exercise."

But the experience of NEST grew up from a number of nuclear disasters, some of which took place more than a decade before it was actually created. One was of major proportion and would, in climate and terrain, be related to the conditions of Operation Morning Light.

On January 21, 1965, a B52 aircraft bomber nick-named Hobo 28 was flying a twenty-four hour airborne alert mission over Greenland when she caught fire due to an electrical failure. Five of the six men who bailed out survived the harrowing ordeal, and the plane crashed on the sea ice near the town of Thule. But it wasn't an ordinary crash. The B52 carried in its hold four plutonium bombs. There were some conventional-type explosions of non-radioactive material as the aircraft disintegrated and burned on impact, but fortunately the nuclear bombs didn't explode. Moreover, the bomber crashed far from any habitation: the land was barren, almost empty of anything except nomadic Eskimo hunters and a remote United States Air Force base at Thule, part of the Strategic Air Command. The plutonium was spread like jelly over a large area of the sea ice.

Thus started the little-known and highly dramatic "Project Crested Ice," launched in cooperation with the Danish authorities who administer Greenland. The radioactive material dispersed on the offshore pack ice posed a serious and unknown contamination hazard. To recover and remove it, health physicists and scientists from the Lawrence Livermore Laboratory near San Francisco hastily formed into a team. Widespread contamination of the ice, some of which was seventeen miles from the impact area, was removed by man power. Later on, machine loaders scooped up the surface snow and placed it in large sealed metal containers that were put onboard a navy cargo freighter at Thule. Finally the contaminated snow and aircraft debris were shipped to California for laboratory testing and eventual disposal. The task took over three months in temperatures as low as $-40°$. And it was a complicated, difficult operation. Equipment froze, wires became so brittle they broke into small pieces, and new techniques for external battery packs which housed infrared and gamma-ray detectors had to be adapted. The gamma and neutron monitoring principles developed at Thule were to become part of a basic procedure for NEST. Lessons learned there would be invaluable for the future.

The Thule disaster came at a time when the Lawrence Livermore Laboratory had been experimenting with their FIDLER (Field Instrument for Detection of Low Energy Radiation). This was fortunate. But it was also becoming clear that the Air Force Disaster Response Force was inadequate on its own to deal with accidental nuclear emergencies. One other fact stood out from the Thule experience. There was no such thing as full protection. No matter how complete the precautions, no matter how good the safety records of nuclear weapons plants or test sites, an accident was possible. A person or a machine at a given moment could fail under stress. The computers might rate the chance of error as one in a million, but sooner or later that one chance would spin around on the gigantic wheel that determines the fortunes of mankind.

This point was made again in 1970, when another B52 bomber with nuclear weapons crashed off the coast of Palomares, Spain. A regular task force had to be created by the United States, still the most powerful nuclear nation in the world.

As a result of these machine failures, the growing proliferation of nuclear material, and the ease with which one could make a small atomic bomb, Gates slowly began to build his system of prevention and detection. It would come under the jurisdiction of the FBI, and its task would be to prevent and neutralize all nuclear threats other than military. And if a disaster did occur the new force would be put at the disposal of any private institution or nation. "Broken Arrows" became the code-name for accidents involving nuclear explosives. And Gates, a proud man, wanted to be proud of the organization he was asked to build.

After studying Project Crested Ice, the NEVOO manager familiarized himself with the possible role of terrorist organizations like the Baader Meinhof Gang and threats that originated from individuals in his own country. His grasp of the subject became quite formidable. He was an able administrator, and under him he had access to some of the best scientific brains in the nation. He could draw upon scientists from Los Alamos, Albuquerque, the University of California, and a number of captive companies. Under Gates, the United States would prepare itself to meet the threat of any wanton nuclear catastrophe.

The Atomic Energy Act, a four-inch-thick document that defines in painful detail the penalties, safeguards, use and purpose of everything connected with atomic energy in the United States, provided for a vast security network covering all nuclear operations. All the findings of research programs would be guarded zealously. The FBI had increased surveillance on all nuclear establishments to prevent the theft of enriched uranium or plutonium. But they would be helpless without a trained scientific team who could detect the presence of any nuclear material in the hands of thieves. And as the United States nuclear stockpile grew, as more nations built their own devices, so the danger of accidents increased. The bomb that John Aristotle Phillips designed as a class project could be made by a lot of other undergraduates. Also, the number of space vehicles that belonged to the United States and the Soviet Union grew at a tremendous rate. And some of these satellites carried nuclear reactors. A space vehicle collision in space at certain periods was a possibility. Synchronous satellites are launched into a 22,000 mile orbit over the equator. Too many synchronous satellites bring closer the possibility of a nuclear crash high above the earth. By 1985, the number of man-made earth satellites could rise to over 10,000. And this figure might be conservative.

After the NEST 77 exercise, one particular shortcoming became apparent. NEST required a full complement of equipment and personnel to be ready on a twenty-four-hour standby basis. The team had to be prepared at short notice to go where the danger lay. But that required money. The head of NEVOO realized that due to budgetary cycles it would probably be 1979 or 1980 before he could request the vital funding. Some important event that would bring NEST to the attention of the Congressional authorities would leave no doubt as to its usefulness. Gates believed there were still people in high places who didn't appreciate the importance of NEST. Since its formation the emergencies had been of a local nature: industrial companies losing a small quantity of radioactive material or some nuclear establishment requesting a detection team to look for radiation leaks. The conventional organizations would have been quite capable of dealing with these hazards. NEST required a major test to prove its worth. Yet secretly Gates must have hoped that day would never arrive.

NEST has become the overseer of operation doomsday. Under the reassuring and kindly Mahlon Gates, doomsday would be as comforting as possible. Physicists, mathematicians, chemists, engineers, geophysicists and biologists chosen to represent the NEST organization became the super elite of the American nuclear community. None of the team are under military discipline but are, as Gates takes great care in explaining, a civilian organization. They are all dedicated, committed volunteers. When asked what would happen if any members of the team should refuse an assignment, Gates dismisses the question. "That is unlikely to occur."

One morning two weeks before Christmas, 1977, Troy Wade slipped unannounced into Gates' office in Las Vegas. Wade is the Assistant Manager of NEVOO and Gates' close deputy; most of the day-to-day working management of the office is under his supervision. He is a thin, athletic-looking man with a rather serene, narrow face trimmed by a small, black goatee. On that December day he wore an open-necked shirt and had a rather solemn expression. Outside the morning sun flooded the streets, and snow on the distant mountain peaks reflected the dazzlingly clear light of the desert. The crowds of gamblers were beginning to drift wearily away from the casinos after their usual all-night gaming sessions.

Wade startled Gates by asking, in hushed tones, "Do you mind if I close the door?"

Gates, surprised, nodded his agreement. He seldom closes his office door and the request was most unusual.

"I've just had a phone call," Wade said. He intimated it had come through DOE's secret communication system.

Gates was still puzzled by his deputy's approach. It was unusually stiff, almost formal. Very odd in an office where relations between members of the staff were kept on an easy, informal first-name basis.

Wade continued in the same low voice. "I've been told that a satellite belonging to the USSR, powered by a nuclear reactor, is expected to impact the earth between April and June of 1978. NEST must be ready."

April was four months away. There was no hurry. The whereabouts of the NEST team were always known, and they could be notified in minutes. Moreover, Wade assured his superior that a hazards analysis had already been made, and the chance of the satellite crashing on land rather than water was very small.

Nevertheless, if that chance came up NEST would have to be ready to go into action. The orbits were passing regularly over the North American continent, and the satellite could cause grave damage if it landed in any built-up area. But no one would know for some time exactly where the object would come down – not until it began to decay on its last dying orbits in the earth's atmosphere. The challenge to the organization could be immense. As Wade commented that morning, there were few really solid facts known about the spacecraft. Later when Gates would look back over the weeks and recall his scientists working under the hardest conditions to which they had ever been exposed he would say, "We were extending peoples' endurance pretty thoroughly, beyond what one thought possible. They responded beautifully." He was satisfied that his men were meeting their sternest challenge.

NEST was unencumbered by any formal military structure, but for a major emergency which Cosmos could present there was a certain hierarchy of administrative and scientific command. The logical scientific leader would be someone like Richard Wagner, the Associate Director of the Lawrence Livermore Laboratory in California.

Wade would be the day-to-day operating chief representing the DOE and would report to Gates in Las Vegas.

The NEST team would constitute a total of approximately one hundred personnel. Between five and ten were to handle the operational planning, depending on the nature of the emergency. About fifteen people would control and operate communication and logistics equipment. Thirty research scientists were available for improvising and applying special techniques and the remainder would be engineers, electronic technicians and secretaries. Two small helicopters jammed with electronic surveillance gear were always available; these would be carried inside the giant four-motored C141 jet transports which NEST had at its disposal. The transports had a range of 6,000 miles. In addition there were three large aluminum containers on wheels packed with communication equipment. Unmarked bread vans painted a sterile white carried the data processing banks. Each van had a crew of technicians, computers and communication instruments. They were ready at short notice to drive onto the rear loading platforms of the C141s. Several dozen hand-held radiation and infrared counters were also packed and stored and ready to go. Other gamma and neutron detectors, fitted into ordinary attache cases, could be carried inconspicuously by the NEST team into built-up areas. These small emergency packs were known as Los Alamos briefcases.

The scientists had recently added one more innovation, a microwave ranging system. This was a highly accurate navigation system which allowed slow-flying aircraft or helicopters to follow regular grid patterns over precise courses. The grids flown by the planes carrying this equipment could fly over any kind of terrain, covering lines fifty feet or less apart. In this way detection equipment could pick up any ground contamination and later fly back to relocate the source precisely. But the great strength of NEST lay in its ability to improvise. No exercise could precisely duplicate the one before. And no real danger was predictable.

NEVOO was reliably informed that whenever Cosmos landed they would be given the time plus or minus twenty hours. Also, there would be no public mention of the impending disaster. It would be up to the government to alert the people when the hour arrived, but no one knew whose responsibility that would be. It was still too early to get excited, but Gates and Wade couldn't help feeling a tremor of anxiety at the prospect of having to call upon the full capabilities of NEST. But in December that idea was remote, unreal. A landing on water was the most likely possibility. If that didn't happen, Cosmos could burn itself out as it broke against the barrier of the earth's atmosphere.

Yet in spite of all the learned predictions the men in Las Vegas watched Cosmos with a growing sense of excitement. There would be no useful purpose served in frightening people about a nuclear disaster if the chance of its happening was so small. There were, however, a number of advocates who didn't favor this approach. One was Barnett Danson, the Canadian Minister of Defense. "If necessary," he said subsequently, "we should publish a book as thick as a telephone directory with all the names of towns where the object might strike."

Gates' attitude was completely different. He favored secrecy – a clandestine military operation. He felt the situation would be much more manageable this way. An emergency was building up. A crisis was looming, coming faster than anyone knew at the time. The fear had been expressed to Gates that the 100-pound enriched uranium core could, under certain conditions, heat up and approach criticality. This would make Cosmos an atomic bomb at least as powerful as the one that demolished Hiroshima. Gates must have shuddered at the thought. The emergency was distant, yet there was a certain momentum developing in the NEST organization as the state of preparedness advanced and all key personnel were secretly notified to stand by. As Gates said, "there was a considerable state of alert among the agencies concerned." This meant not only NEST, but also the army, the CIA, the FBI and the special Washington committee over which Zbigniew Brzezinski presided. There was one other organization involved, the little-known Federal Preparedness Agency. In December Gates had taken one of its representatives quietly onto his staff. This man appeared on the scene only at times of national emergencies. He was an expert on coordinating the resources of the country when events reached cataclysmic proportions.

As Cosmos' dying orbits spun it over the United States those few people in NEST who were given the daily predicted track of the space vehicle were very worried men. What was on

Gates' mind was on the mind of everyone who waited for the final orbit. "In the United States, we would be faced with a problem of tremendous magnitude. In addition to finding the pieces we have the crisis management to take care of. The more the fragmentation the greater the hazard."

With outward calm, Gates awaited the final moment.

4

Throughout the month of January, Cosmos lost more and more of its orbital rhythm and continued to move steadily westward. On the 21st it skimmed the atmosphere close to Miami, ricocheted back into space, passed over Detroit and then, as if controlled by some invisible, whimsical hand, on a succeeding orbit crossed above Las Vegas. When informed of the pass above Las Vegas, Troy Wade thought that perhaps he should begin unpacking the NEST emergency vehicles (parked then at DOE headquarters in the city) and prepare for an emergency at home. Even though there was still no way of knowing where the satellite would come down, the date of impact had been moved up drastically: Cosmos was not going to crash in April or June but within a matter of days – some time in the last week of January.

The Soviet authorities no longer pretended they had control of the vehicle. The informal committee set up by America's National Security Council applied increasing pressure for relevant information. But none was forthcoming. For the time being nothing much could be done except to intensify the state of alert. To facilitate its work the committee included a representative of the Department of Energy. If there should be inquiries about the purpose of the newly formed group, the official explanation was that there had been "a space age difficulty . . . there is no danger."

The heads of government in the United Kingdom, France, Italy, Germany, Canada and Japan were secretly notified; some of these nations cooperated in tracking Cosmos' progress. But the United States felt that, as the mightiest power in the west, it had a major responsibility to the free world. No nation except Russia was so committed to the nuclear way of life. The United States possessed the equipment to follow Cosmos' orbit of the world and felt it could deal with it when it came down. The chance that a satellite with a nuclear reactor might enter the atmosphere over America brought the thought of a space disaster close to home for the first time in history. The prospect of an uncontrollable reentry of an enemy satellite over North America was awesome, ominous. In the military mind it produced aggressive responses, perhaps not all of them on a conscious level. After all, Russia had still made no comment, either official or unofficial. In fact, there was a peculiar silence in Moscow. This could be serious: silence breeds speculation, and speculation concerning unidentified enemy objects orbiting in space can instigate a whole series of suspicious, dangerous reactions. There were a number of people in the Pentagon who conjectured that maybe the Russians were testing NORAD's defenses and that Cosmos had been deliberately redirected in its orbit to pass over some of the early warning systems. The 110 pounds of enriched uranium 235 in the satellite core bred some wild speculation in the minds of those who knew about the runaway satellite. The half-life of the fissionable material in the satellite's core (that is, the time it would take half the material to lose its radioactivity) was rated by some at 500 million years.

With the satellite's impact definitely due to occur within a couple of days, continuing attention was paid to predicting exactly where and when it would reenter the atmosphere. As Troy Wade had told General Gates, the time of the crash could be determined within twenty hours plus or minus. But the science of prediction was still an imperfect one. Of prime importance was the location of the satellite's "footprint": the impact site, dispersal region of fragments (if it struck land), and the relative position of the radioactive core. But the footprint could only be accurately charted when Cosmos began to decay and reenter the atmosphere – not before.

On January 21, Joseph Tinney, NEST member and head of the National Resource Evaluation program at Lawrence Livermore, was notified by his chief, Richard Wagner, to stand by for an emergency. The next day, Sunday, Tinney said goodbye to his wife and family. He would miss the soccer game with his son which offered him a few relaxing hours of exercise on the weekend. Then the scientist left for a meeting of the DOE Emergency Action Coordinating Team – a part of NEST – at Germantown, Pennsylvania. Russell Lease, the biologist from DOE and head of their Eastern Office, was waiting for Tinney. They were to be ready to go to nearby Andrews Air Force Base, where a C141 loaded with detection equipment was on the runway.

At this point, no one in the NEST team knew their ultimate destination. They would be leaving for somewhere in the Western Hemisphere, but that was all they would know until Cosmos started its decay and began its final plunge toward earth. They hoped some visual sightings would be available to corroborate the exact position of the satellite's reentry. A steady stream of secret phone calls was now going out over the private telephone system of the Las Vegas office to the entire NEST team.

By mid-January a consensus had grown among the aerospace engineers attached to NEST that Cosmos' most likely course of reentry would be into the northern part of North America. But the authorities remained silent. No one wanted to be the first to inform the public of a possible space disaster before the disaster struck. This bureaucratic condescension later aroused deep criticism among many Canadians, a bitter resentment that they were denied vital information. Some authorities envisaged an exodus of gigantic proportions from the threatened areas if the worst predictions were realized. In fact, it would soon be seen that silence would have had the effect of intensifying the fears of the public. Only the President of the United States or the Canadian Prime Minister could make the decision to break the news and both of these men, until the very last day, were fed only part of the facts.

NEST, however, was fully aware. Gates had set the emergency machinery in motion to a level just below a general alert in mid-January. The FBI and CIA had notified emergency contacts through their own secret communication system in every town in the United States. Perhaps the thought of a space disaster on earth was too preposterous for anyone to believe. Somehow, what happened out of sight in space was unreal.

Twice, once on January 12 and again on January 17, Zbigniew Brzezinski had conferred with the Russian Ambassador to the United States, Anatoli Dobrynin. Dobrynin, himself a former aerodynamic engineer, knew a good deal about the construction of Cosmos. But neither Dobrynin nor any other Soviet official was very helpful. They would only confirm that "Cosmos 954 was not an atomic bomb," and Dobrynin told Brzezinski that there was no way in which the satellite's uranium power pack could reach critical mass as it sliced into the atmosphere, thus producing the intense heat required to set off an atomic chain reaction. But other than that the Russians gave no particulars about the enrichment of the uranium. Nor did they say anything about the weight and construction of the satellite; this would have removed much of the guesswork about any potential danger and been of tremendous help to the Americans trying to plot Cosmos' reentry. On the whole, the Soviet–American meetings were friendly but nervous. No one was absolutely sure whether the other was telling the whole truth, or what important information was being held in reserve. The details would be left to the experts. Meanwhile, day by day, hour by hour, Cosmos was drawing closer to the earth and its orbits were swinging over the North American continent.

One of the NEST experts is William Ayres, a health physicist who lectures on radiation fallout hazards to United States Air Force personnel. He is a Texan who lived for a time in Arkansas and has the characteristics of both states. His blond hair is cropped short; he talks in a peaceful, calm drawl and chews plug tobacco. Lately he has developed a small paunch from too much desk work and good living. Like the remainder of the NEST team, he wondered what all the excitement was about when he received his phone call from Las Vegas to stand by. He takes real nuclear hazards in much the same easy way that he offers his advice to military personnel about the event of nuclear conflict.

Ayres doesn't waste many words. When asked what he would recommend if Cosmos broke through the atmosphere over Miami and fragmented, his comment was brief:

"My recommendation would be to evacuate the goddamned place."

5

In the early 1930s, the great scientist Ernest Lawrence did pioneering work in high-energy physics at the University of California. Today it seems fitting that his name should ornament the Lawrence Livermore Laboratory, the top-secret research establishment where the neutron bomb was conceived.

The laboratory buildings are surrounded by sun-parched lawns, tall flowering palms and a high barbed wire fence. A small bungalow at the entrance is staffed by secretaries, guards and has a compact conference room with blackboard, used for visitors who for one reason or another cannot obtain security clearance to enter the main compound. Lawrence Livermore is not permitted to host foreigners except under the most extraordinarily stringent conditions. Strict rules of conduct are laid down by the Atomic Energy Act and enforced by the FBI. Anyone foreign pretending to be an American and allowed to enter would, upon discovery, be subject to immediate deportation. There is a holy respect for rules and security among the two thousand employees in this mile-square complex dominated by the tall gray stone mathematics and physics building at the entrance.

As the *Energy and Technology Review* of the laboratory states, some of the main objectives of the organization are to make "headway toward greater weapons safety by reducing the probability that a warhead's high explosive component would detonate accidentally. Toward the same end we continued work on a practical scheme for protecting nuclear materials and preventing the dispersal of radioactive material in any circumstance other than intentional warhead detonation."

These principles govern much of the thinking of a forty-two-year-old Phi Beta Kappa scientist named Richard Wagner, the Associate Director at Lawrence Livermore Laboratories, and a member of NEST. Ever since 1963, when he took his PhD at the University of Utah, Wagner has spent his entire working career at Livermore. His research background concentrated on cosmic rays, high-energy physics, nuclear explosives design, weapons effects and anti-ballistic missiles systems studies. He has risen to his present position from being an ordinary staff member; along the way he held the titles of Program Manager and Division Leader.

Wagner's dedication, loyalty and intimate grasp of the entire nuclear weapons program have helped make him part of the new scientific breed who are at the top of the nuclear business. Like most of his colleagues, he has a governor built into his personality: this restrains his conversation, telling him what can be disclosed and what cannot. But within the limits of this restraint, Wagner is remarkably lucid and informative. He is small, rather dapper, always well dressed, and has slightly hollowed cheeks. There is a formality in his appearance – a premeditated yet natural politeness. His manner is sharp, to the point. He speaks precisely and illustrates his remarks, whenever possible, with diagrams. When speaking of organizations and involved subjects he likes to draw them out on the blackboard so there can be no mistakes. He is sympathetic and tolerant, and he listens carefully to all but unnecessary explanations. He is quick to correct a statement and impatient with those less lucid than himself. But he is under control at all times.

Wagner is a child of the post-Oppenheimer generation of nuclear physicists who no longer question the morality of the United States nuclear program. Loyalty to the program is paramount: men like Wagner have grown up on it. He is privy to the most guarded secrets of the Army Scientific Advisory Group. Under the Department of Energy, Wagner was no doubt the most suitable candidate to lead the NEST team when Cosmos 954 re-entered the earth's atmosphere. He is also eminently qualified to describe the functions of NEST, which he did for me the first time I spoke to him.

"If there is an accident involving a nuclear weapon or with a US reactor, there is a cleanup function to be performed. The last time this was done was when that B52 crashed at the Thule Air Force Base in Greenland in 1965. We found our ability to respond to situations like that pretty limited. In the process of developing our capability, this laboratory put together what was known as a 'hot spot team.' Then about three or four years ago we began to realize there were somewhat broader problems with nuclear energy than just accident problems. For instance, what happens in a situation where a nuclear storage weapons site is overrun and someone gets a weapon. Everything became combined under NEST."

Among the elite of DOE's laboratories in Livermore and Los Alamos, and among the DOE's captive scientific establishments, Wagner is looked upon as a leader. Sometimes he briefly concerns himself with what he calls, for lack of a more meaningful expression, "the trade-off." In analyzing the trade-off in any situation, Wagner weighs its end result against its social repercussions. The nuclear elite are not inclined to indulge in anything that might be construed as sentiment. Nor are they very adept at explorations of thought that reach into the philosophical. Nevertheless, they have to strike a balance between the possible harm done to man by radiation fallout and what Wagner and his colleagues conceive as the national good for defense.

In Wagner's view, there were two extremes of danger if the object struck land. "The entire reactor core could come down intact. That's a highly radioactive object. This core has a total inventory of activity in the order of a 100,000 curies. If you come closer than a thousand feet you very rapidly get into a radiation field which can give out a lot of danger-damage."

He went on to expound tersely the second hazard. "A fragment the size of a bean you could stay five feet away from. If you had it in your pocket you could get a dose, not lethal but more than you would like to get." Wagner seemed to have the dangers of Cosmos 954 pretty well summed up. He and his NEST team would be as well prepared as anyone could be for the emergency.

It would be difficult to find the core of Cosmos in a reasonably uninhabited area. "Radiation is attenuated very rapidly by air. With a pretty sensitive radiation detector you would have a 20 percent chance of finding the core in the first ten days. Compared to the immense destructive power of the warheads the core of Cosmos is a modest hazard."

During the last days of Cosmos Wagner was given the reports of the satellite's trajectory on a daily basis as they came off the computers. In Livermore the task of predicting the reentry was assigned to NEST members Milo Bell, a bespectacled engineer, and his more slightly-built comrade Ira Morrison, a defense analysis mathematician. They would do their work on a Control Data Corporation 7600, one of the most advanced computers in the world.

Bell and Morrison are part of the California T-shirt brigade: they have no executive responsibilities like Wagner to fulfill, so dress is of no importance. Everything is casual except their attitude toward security. If one accidentally enters a forbidden zone of conversation the talk falters, hesitates, and then continues on a different subject. Most members of this close community look over their shoulders, metaphorically at least, when they discuss their work with strangers.

For Bell and Morrison the task of computing the trajectory of Cosmos as it approached the atmosphere meant applying themselves continuously, day and night. The big CDC 7600 was placed exclusively at their disposal until the job was done. They had to feed into the complicated machine a tremendous array of detailed figures in which the unknowns considerably exceeded the known factors.

Bell made some quick hand calculations on January 20, at the beginning of their intensive work. With the available data Bell built up a rough picture of the footprint – the path along which the satellite would land and fragment. If Cosmos fragmented this would be the "worst case" situation. For each one tenth of a second that the satellite moved along its orbital flight path the men devised a mathematical model of the object and a possible impact zone. At this early stage, Bell and Morrison could already predict the width and length of the area of impact. In the "worst case," Cosmos could splatter over a district 50 to 60 miles wide and about 500 to 600 miles long. This projection was to prove uncannily accurate; for a long time it remained unchanged.

Bell contacted some of his friends at the Lockheed Aircraft Corporation in nearby Sunnyvale, who take part in the design and construction of guided missiles and space craft. Based on their own vehicles, and on some information they possessed about comparable Soviet craft, they offered possible design characteristics of Cosmos. The weight, length and power source of similar United States satellites suggested important clues. Even with these clues, however, the task was truly formidable for the two men who had not worked out any problems on the CDC 7600 for many months.

It didn't take more than a few hours to reacquaint themselves with the huge computer, but Morrison was somewhat saddened at the beginning. He was presently building an exotic Bugetta dune buggy whose completion had been deferred many times because of the pressure of work. Now he would have to wait until the emergency was over before he could continue. He didn't think it would last very long. A few days, at the most. Bell, who normally rides to work on a bicycle, canceled all his private after-hours work as a consultant for lawyers and insurance companies in the assessing of claims involving industrial machinery. These two NEST members, in spite of their air of nonchalance, are highly qualified, inventive and well suited to their role in plotting the demise of Cosmos 954.

In their workroom at Livermore, Bell and Morrison marked off a map of the world into segments, with certain segments denoting those areas where Cosmos was most likely to enter the atmosphere in its decay. NORAD periodically supplied information in what is called the satellite's "state vector" – its latitude, longitude, speed and direction. These were the only data the two computer experts could be certain of at any time. Using whatever additional information they could get, Bell and Morrison applied themselves to the problem for a minimum of ten hours a day. They thought about Cosmos most of the night. If one of them had a new idea he would telephone the other at any hour.

When Bell rode to work at 7:30 AM on Friday, January 21, in the warm, bright California sunshine he was unusually distracted. His mind was not on the road ahead but on how he and his colleague could quickly solve their problem. They were having difficulties: it was more complex than either had originally thought. Bell was determined to resolve it, but the range of variables seemed to grow rather than diminish. The combinations of places Cosmos could crash were almost numberless. The footprint which he had produced so quickly he no longer felt confident about. The long hours of work were already beginning to tell.

When the satellite struck the earth's atmosphere it would slow down considerably, but it could still be compared to a locomotive smashing at 1600 miles an hour through a four-foot-thick concrete wall. Cosmos would enter as a whole, then it could fragment into a few pieces or a million. It might even vaporize without a trace and create a cloud of radioactivity high in the atmosphere. They worked on what they called the strength parameters – the altitudes and velocities at which the satellite might come apart due to different amounts of aerodynamic stress. This indicated how far fragments would be carried along the footprint in the "worst case" situation.

On January 22 and 23, Bell and Morrison worked a twenty-hour day. They knew they had to grapple with one of the most difficult problems they ever faced. In the past there had not been the same desperate sense of urgency; nor had the difficulties ever been of the same magnitude. There was usually enough time to work out solutions in normal office hours. But not now. There was an immediate danger that Cosmos could miss the mass of water that covered three quarters of the globe and strike land. The two men had to estimate the exact orbit of the satellite based on a "non-dimensional range curve." This meant, in simple terms, that the curve of the satellite was irregular and unstable. The "non-dimensional range curve" might give another lead as to where Cosmos would go once inside the atmosphere.

From their own calculations, Bell and Morrison estimated

that Cosmos was presently orbiting 115 miles above the earth, plus or minus five miles. It was decelerating at a small but significant rate, and had slowed down to the point where it was now spinning around the earth every eighty-seven minutes. Radar, telescopic and other sightings determined that it was (as of January 23) continuing to move 20 degrees westward with each successive orbit. This movement made the job of determining the region of the crash difficult enough; but there was still no way of computing the effect of the wind. While there was no wind in space, in the atmosphere jet streams could attain speeds of several hundred miles an hour.

Bell, with his aerospace training, kept making a steady stream of inquiries across the nation at space laboratories, universities, anywhere he would find specialists with the appropriate knowledge. Lockheed was one of the most helpful institutions, having built various spacecraft for the United States space program. Other classified information from which Bell could make a good prognosis was slowly, gradually built up. A good deal of guesswork was required but the two men believed that in the end they would come close to the truth. The consensus suggested the satellite should burn up on reentry, but no one was absolutely sure. A handful of scientists held that there was a slender chance that part of the machine would survive.

Meanwhile, the tumbling, uncontrolled vehicle continued to hurtle itself wildly around the world. Bell and Morrison continued to go without sleep as they worked toward the solution to their problem. They had divulged to no one – not even their wives – the reason for their late hours and deep fatigue. Even Jeffrey Garberson, the public relations chief at Livermore, who usually knew everything that went on, had no idea what the two men were doing. No announcements could be made to press or associates. The curtain of secrecy over the entire project remained and would stay to the last moment.

For four days Bell and Morrison had hardly returned home

except to snatch a few hours of rest or a decent meal. Most of the time they ate in the laboratory cafeteria and dozed before the monstrous computer that had become a part of their lives. Bell's home was barely five miles from the laboratory, but after a long day and night session calculating endless propositions and studying new varieties of formulas, he could hardly pedal the distance on his bicycle. He awoke tired at dawn each day and, with the equally determined Morrison, would start the simulations anew. The data were endlessly punched into the almost human CDC 7600, which now behaved as if it were in charge of the hunt for Cosmos.

By the night of January 23, as Cosmos 954 wiggled and spun perilously above millions of unaware Americans, a certain recurring pattern was beginning to form on the graph. The figures were narrowing, the parameters shriveling. The coordinates of a certain flight path were reappearing on the computer screen with growing regularity. And the probability that they indicated was frightening to Bell and Morrison, who by this time had shed the light-hearted banter with which they commenced the project. The last orbits of Cosmos 954 were bringing it over the North American continent more and more frequently. From the relatively scanty information with which they began their theorizing, the men came up with one set of figures which they felt they could put their faith into. Understandably, they were a little nervous about the prediction and would have liked to hedge their bets, but fatigue made them less careful than usual. The same wide swath, about thirty miles in diameter and six hundred miles long, was designated as the pathway along which the flaming satellite would burst through the atmosphere and impact the earth – that is, if any of the machine survived. Their original hypothesis was confirmed. They now had to place the footprint on the map of the world.

At 2:00 AM on January 24, Milo Bell was telephoned at the laboratory – Cosmos was on its last orbit. For eighty-seven minutes the engineer felt he hardly breathed. The spacecraft took a last, decaying swing over the South Pole in 64 degree latitude, hurtling in a northeasterly direction.

NORAD contacted Livermore on the open urgent line. It had important news. Reentry of the Russian satellite would commence at exactly 3:56 AM Pacific Standard Time. Impact was scheduled for 4:17 AM in the same time zone. The last vector given began at 64 degrees south latitude and 118 degrees east longitude. This last bit of intelligence went into the great computer and a final simulation result was displayed. Minutes later Cosmos suddenly vanished from radar screens around the world. At 4:30 AM Californian time, the satellite, like a flaming supersonic jet, emitting a strong blue vaporous trail, exploded upon the earth not far from where man had first created the monster.

Bell and Morrison relaxed briefly. They could do no more. Later in the day the simulation was further refined to match additional measured positions along the final reentry trajectory. At this initial stage the outer boundaries of the search area was defined. Constant refinements continued for the next forty-eight hours, but the path was now clear. The footprint of Cosmos went through the far-off forsaken wastes of the Northwest Territories of Canada.

Milo Bell and Ira Morrison checked their map. The only town they could see which was close to the footprint was called Yellowknife. It sat alone on the western end of the Great Slave Lake in a country where lakes, more numerous than one could count, lay strewn like laced pearls over tens of thousands of square miles. Bell, out of curiosity, checked on weather conditions in Yellowknife. It was −50° with a wind factor of 20 making the true temperature −70°. The mere thought of this made him shiver: he was still wearing an open necked shirt.

At 3:30 PM on January 25, an ad hoc "trajectory dynamics working group" met at Livermore. The groggy Bell and Morrison attended the session more asleep than awake. Representatives of Sandia, Lockheed and the Aerospace Corporation were present. All organizations had their own computer calculations which differed from the two Livermore men but only in minor details. For sixteen hours representatives of the four large laboratories argued, doubted and tried to find a common location. The Livermore solution was the most complete. But the

45

conversations and computers in California were not producing the one result everyone in the world sought: the precise
location of Cosmos. There would be only one positive way of
finding out, and that was to go up to Canada and search for
debris. Once a major fragment was found, Bell and Morrison
would know their calculations were correct. But they wouldn't
know until then. There were sure to be a number of strange
anomalies about this enormous region in the north that no one
in the relaxing warmth of Livermore could fully imagine.

Four days before Cosmos came down General Mahlon Gates in
Las Vegas had contacted his superior in Washington, General
Joseph Bratton, on the secure telephone system. Bratton and
Gates were old army friends and Gates would not have to explain the emergency in detail. Bratton had been kept informed
daily of the situation and had expected a call for days. It came
at 8:00 AM Washington time on January 20. The deputy manager, Troy Wade, awakened Gates at home. The emergency was
on. Gates in turn immediately called Bratton. No one apologized
for the early hour. It was five o'clock in the morning in Las
Vegas and the Strip was illuminated as brilliantly as a clear
desert day.

"Joe," Gates said to his superior in Washington after a brief
greeting, "I need five C141s."

These large military jets were each capable of carrying a
small helicopter and tiers of NEST's special equipment and fifty
people. They cruised at 600 miles per hour.

Gates gave further particulars. "I want two planes at
McCarran at Las Vegas, two at Ellis and one at Andrews in
Washington standing by."

"You've got them," Bratton replied without hesitation.

"Furthermore, I want the loadmasters ready to move at
2:00 PM Sunday, January 22."

"What's going onto the planes?" Bratton asked.

"Everything we have. Our total capability."

"Is it that serious?" Bratton persisted.

"Yes," came the terse reply. "I think it is."

Still the secret was maintained. Only a few key members of the NEST team had been informed by Wade who in turn had contacted Wagner at Livermore and the biologist Russell Lease of the Department of Energy. The heads of government in England, France, Italy, Germany and Canada were informed as well as Japan who had a very special sensitivity to nuclear danger, being the only country who had actually experienced a nuclear catastrophe first hand. Gates knew that with every additional hour came the growing possibility that NEST would be applying their skills on their own continent. The chance that the satellite would strike somewhere in Siberia had also been considered, since the orbits had been moving steadily to the west. If that happened NEST would stand down and no one would ever know what happened to Cosmos.

Russell Lease and his small team gathered at Andrews Air Force Base set off for the Canadian Forces Base at Edmonton on January 23. They came largely from Livermore and EG&G (Egerton, Grier and Germanhausen), a hugely successful company started by a group of scientists who had been employed by the US Government during World War II. Its laboratories had made significant advances in the field of radiation detection. Lease himself worked for the DOE office since 1972. His card says "Manager, Eastern Measurements Office." It doesn't mention what he measures. Lease is a New Englander who loves the outdoor life of hunting and fishing. The thought of traveling to the far Northwest Territories did not disturb him: in fact, he was rather looking forward to the experience. Slow, careful in speech, round-faced and bespectacled, he mixes easily with people. Like his compatriots he is proud of his work and believes deeply in the nuclear commitment.

Lease had worked on the Enewetak project helping to clean up this small atoll in the Marshall Islands. As a biologist he is very much concerned with the recycling of radioactive material into the animal and plant food chain. In the Pacific he studied marine life around the contaminated atolls. Lease had no idea what to expect in northern Canada. All he knew was that it

47

would be very cold and that Cosmos had already ripped through the atmosphere above Yellowknife.

Lease would be among the first of the NEST personnel to arrive at the destination.

Part Two

THE COLD SEARCH

6

In the shining night sky of Canada's Northwest Territories the trillions of celestial bodies are so close together that they look like solid rivers of molten light. This illusion is intensified by the magnificent clarity of the air. Settlers came here to seek the freedom of space and leave civilization behind forever. They thought that when the roads ended and the towns stopped they would have the peace they sought.

Over the centuries these lands have come to be known as the Barren Lands, or simply the Barrens. Although they look peaceful this is a misleading impression. No land has so savage a history. The English explorers Sir John Franklin and George Back experienced the brutality of the terrain when they walked hundreds of miles over the desolate landscape between 1819 and 1822, much of it in winter in −60° weather. The punishing hardships they endured drove the small band of explorers almost beyond the extreme limits of human endurance. They survived only with the help of their Indian guides. Now, people have learned to live off a land which looks at first as if this were an impossible task. It is difficult to locate the abundant animal and fish life, but it is there. Sometimes the fish move to new rivers, the caribou take different trails and the ptarmigans fly beyond the reach of a gun. In spring the Barren grizzlies hungrily roam the country. They are fierce, ugly, ill-tempered; they live in caves hollowed out in the sides of the big pingos − massive upheavals of tundra caused by frost action. In summer the mosquitoes and black flies drive the caribou wild and inflict merciless punishment on anyone who dares expose the tiniest part of his flesh.

There are few towns in the middle of the Barrens. The

breadth of this infinitude of lakes, rivers, stunted pine trees, rocky chasms, hidden gorges and raging waterfalls is like a vision of a land time has forgotten. In the winter there is absolute silence for long periods. The crack of a frozen twig in the brittle air can carry across the frozen lakes for miles. The howl of a timber wolf echoes interminably down the ice-packed rivers, lingering in the night like a faint whisper, finally dying across the Barrens. In the midst of this inhospitable winter environment one might just hear the distant chug of a snowmobile belonging to some Chipewyan Indian hunter, or see the clouds of billowing snow churned up by its treads.

But no hunter, however ingenious a mechanic he might be, will take a chance in the wilderness with his snowmobile alone. He will usually be accompanied by a companion with a dog team. Fuel gives out, so does food. If the herds of caribou, which many of the hunting families depend on for sustenance, change their migration habits they can be missed altogether. When starvation faces a hunter, which is not an infrequent occurrence on a long journey, he will eat his dogs if necessary, for survival. His snowmobile he will leave until summer and then carry it back to his village piece by piece.

There is more water north of the sixtieth parallel than land. The nameless clusters of lakes are carelessly strung together by as many nameless rivers. In January the rivers are white sinews that thread the quiet winter wilderness. In the short summer they leap into life, writhing like thrashing serpents through the Barrens.

One of the biggest lakes, Great Slave Lake, is 380 miles long and at its widest 60 miles across. Yellowknife sits alone at its western extremity. The Barrens begin some miles beyond the sixtieth parallel which is the northern provincial boundary of Alberta, Saskatchewan and Manitoba. They continue on north through rough strata of natural uranium, potassium and thorium for up to six hundred miles. Where the tree line stops the Eskimos inherit the wilderness.

A few people in Yellowknife who were out early in the morning of January 24 happened by chance to look skyward. They saw a sight that morning they would never forget. Some of those who stumbled through the cold dawn were too drunk to turn their heads skyward or else they too might have seen it. The inhabitants of the Yellowknife district who did stare at the heavens in the pre-dawn of that historic day were stunned and then bewildered by what they saw.

Jimmy Doctor, a Dog Rib Indian, observed the flaming spacecraft and remembered what he had been told by his friend David Sangris. Sangris was an old Indian whose toothless grin and craggy face were well known around Yellowknife. His uncombed white hair straggled down beneath a wide-brimmed black hat. He was a soothsayer, an aged local prophet, a kind of shaman of the Dog Ribs. On July 10, 1975, Sangris was in a particularly talkative mood and told young Jimmy Doctor a story that no one believed. Doctor thought it was only the ramblings of an old man who would soon meet his Maker, and chose not to believe it. But on that hot July night with the mosquitoes and black flies biting with a particular fierceness the young Indian obediently listened to the aged Sangris. It frightened the younger man, but he showed respect for his old friend. Today he remembers the event vividly.

"David Sangris was sitting outside in a chair waiting for a bus so he could go to Weaver's store when I passed by. I asked him what he was sitting outside for. That was when he said, 'Jim, there's something I want to tell you. I won't live long but don't tell anyone, not even your best friend.'" Doctor promised he would obey the old man's wish.

"'Son,' Sangris said, 'you're going to see something, something you've never seen in your life, something with a flame behind it. It's going to happen in the winter. You and a woman from Yellowknife are going to see it. And if this thing comes to Yellowknife there will be lots of Americans here to look for it. Write a story for me after it lands.'"

Then the old prophet ambled away from his young friend without saying another word.

53

Jimmy Doctor recalled, "That night I saw it I was listening to the radio at home when I heard some noise behind the house. So I got up to see what it was. It was a dog howling into the sky beside my skidoo. I looked up into the sky to see if the moon was still shining. That was when I seen the big flame going north east. I ran outside to see what it was. I thought it was a plane on fire. I didn't know what it was. It sounded like air coming out of a tire. That was the way I saw the satellite."

Jimmy Doctor thought about the prophecy on January 24 as the body of flame seared above him in the luminous morning sky. Everything old Sangris said must be the truth. Any man who could predict flame and fire in the sky must be a great man. As Doctor thought about Sangris he wondered what the object was, and whether Sangris in his new life also witnessed the truth of his prophecy.

Marie Ruman cleans out the offices of the Canadian Broadcasting Corporation in Yellowknife. She is a black-haired woman of middle age with the expansive spread that most squaws of her tribe – the Dog Rib tribe – develop after the age of thirty. Marie had arrived home after working all night and was sitting in the truck which she drives. "I thought it was a jet on fire with a flaming jet stream," Marie Ruman said later to the army authorities. "I think it was going to the east. In fact I'm sure that's where it went. Northeast."

The amazing sight stunned Marie Ruman at first. When she recovered she ran into the house to awake her two children. As they came out, sleepily rubbing their eyes, they could just see flaming debris disappearing in the distance, emitting a trail of vapor. The part that looked like a fuselage on fire was deep red. The pieces behind fanned out like the tail of a peacock in a magnificent display of pyrotechnics. The children, now wide-eyed in wonder, rubbed the sleep from their eyes, not sure whether they were dreaming or awake. The disappearing body of the satellite, spluttering and hissing across the cloudless night and enveloped in flame, was a sight of rare and awesome beauty. It was quite unlike anything that Marie or her children had ever seen before. Later she didn't think it was a fuselage of a jet because it was going too fast. It looked quite long and was very difficult to describe. Marie is a simple Indian woman who has lived for many years in the city and the strange experience unnerved her. It was quite beyond her comprehension. It had been a quiet autumn and winter in Yellowknife without any spectacular event to distract the population. And none was contemplated – except the approaching Arctic Games. There would be some fireworks for that, but the games, Marie knew, were many months off.

When the object disappeared, the sleepy, bemused children tramped back through the snow to the small frame house and stumbled into bed. Marie stood out alone for a while in the bitter cold staring at the black sky, but nothing more disturbed the shining firmament. The stars were beginning to dissolve in the gray dawn. There was, thought Marie, an unnatural stillness. Maybe the strange occurrence announced the coming of the Messiah. She was a religious woman. She crossed herself, slammed the door of her truck and tramped over the crisp snow into her home. Whatever it was she saw she would never forget it. She was so nervous she hardly slept more than a few hours that night.

Later in the day, when Marie heard on the radio about all the excitement created by the entry into the earth's atmosphere of a Russian satellite in the Yellowknife area, she telephoned the Northern Command of the Canadian Forces located in the town. Almost immediately an officer visited her and asked many questions about the direction, shape and characteristics of the thing she saw. That day Marie was deluged with calls from reporters, some of whom were in Edmonton and others in such faraway places as New York, Hawaii and Paris. The Dog Rib squaw felt she had become a celebrity overnight.

Peter Pagonis delivers tanks of drinking water to the military aircraft hangar at the Yellowknife airport. He left his house on 54th Street before 4:00 that morning, glanced briefly at the sky and suddenly stopped hitching up the water tanks. He looked again. There was no doubt. Three unidentified flying objects streaked across the dark morning sky. They looked bluish red.

The object in front was the largest, like a huge pencil, spurting an incandescent jet of such pure brilliance that Pagonis thought it might be one of those laser beams he had once seen on a television program. The brilliant streaks trailed fiery tails and dove beyond the town in a northeasterly direction. When Pagonis came to the military aircraft hangar and delivered his water that morning he told his story to the corporal on duty.

That same day the phone of Sig Sigvaldason began to ring very early. Sigvaldason, the editor of the local newspaper the *Yellowknifer*, hardly had time to dress before he had his first call. He looked at the gray light filtering through the ice-coated windows of his house as he picked up his receiver in amazement and heard a reporter from the American Broadcasting Corporation in New York asking questions about a Russian satellite. The Americans intended to charter a jet to bring in their own film crew to photograph the satellite in Yellowknife. They wanted first-hand information. When the calm Sigvaldason realized what had happened he explained he could be of no help. A little later, when the British Broadcasting Corporation called and asked whether anyone was searching Great Slave Lake in a boat looking for the enriched uranium core of Cosmos 954, Sigvaldason was better prepared. He had recovered from his initial shock. The editor explained to the caller from London it was impossible to search the lake with a boat since it was frozen and the ice was four feet thick.

From the calls that followed Sigvaldason learned the whole story. Between dressing and drinking his morning coffee he found himself answering inquiries from all over America and Europe.

The stolid, bearded Sigvaldason, who had left the frenzy of the advertising business in Winnipeg to open a small northern newspaper, now found himself in the midst of more excitement than he had experienced for years. Sigvaldason is disdainful of big city people and full of mocking irony about the populace whom he disparagingly refers to as the "southerners." He also has a rather whimsical sense of humor: he decided that morning to write a thank-you note to the Soviet Embassy. Yellowknife was sleeping in the midst of the economic doldrums of winter, and the surge of business from all the media, who would shortly descend upon his city, might provide a most welcome boost for tourist business. Largely empty hotels would raise their low winter rates and the few restaurants would be full again while the somnolent Indians who occasionally drive the taxis in the sub-zero weather could again be gainfully employed.

The big Sigvaldason gave up wearing ties the moment he left Winnipeg and started the *Yellowknifer*, the main newspaper of the town ("Published at least once a week"). He painted his elongated wooden frame building a glaring yellow and wrote in large black letters on a billboard atop the structure: "*Yellowknifer*. Your local Newspaper." And Sigvaldason was in the newspaper business.

The former advertising executive continuously smokes a briar pipe. He is apt to go outside in any weather for brief intervals clad only in a cotton shirt to philosophize with colleagues. He wears glasses and has a patriarchal white beard. Like most Yellowknifers who went north to leave behind their old lives, Sigvaldason doesn't trust "people in the south."

When I spoke to him, he explained his skepticism. "I think we have a different perspective and a greater maturity than the southerners. I refer to the present hysteria. The population is looking in the newspapers for the story of the day, every day. A disaster every hour on the hour."

In a moment of pique, Sigvaldason, irritated by the giant press machines, put the big satellite story on an inside page. Two days after Cosmos landed, below the insignia of a Yellow-knife black raven, the headline in the magazine-sized newspaper referred to an offer by the government to compensate the Indian natives for the use of their land. "Land and millions offer to nations called 'beads and trinkets.'" Sigvaldason refused to be influenced by the flood of world newspapermen who deluged Yellowknife. He kept away from them. He was obsessed at the time with arsenic poisoning in the northern lakes, which is a result of the gold processing (of which arsenic is one of the byproducts). The Giant and Consolidated mines, whose activities for many years have dominated the life in the town, are considered responsible for releasing the arsenic into water around Yellowknife.

When one suggests that Sigvaldason gave indifferent treatment to the potential threat of Cosmos, he looks puzzled, almost hurt. He is not quite sure yet which threat is more harmful, Cosmos or arsenic. He has pronounced views on government, which he mistrusts. "You have to get everything in perspective with arsenic," he keeps reminding the listener. "During this case not only did we lose confidence in credibility of government but we had an opportunity to see how hysteria could be generated without any real foundation."

The big man strokes his beard as he converses and puffs heartily on his pipe. Outdoors, where he sometimes likes to talk on sunlit days, crystals of smoke form a small cloud like a baby atomic mushroom in the clear, cold air. But Sigvaldason is equally comfortable when he can sit in the old swivel chair in his tiny office and discourse on the morality of government.

"Now, our view on satellites is that you can't believe a government. We're so close to government you can't walk down the street without tripping over it. And we realize how little real information is put out and how misleading that information is. The deposit of radioactive materials has a good many dangers. Most of us have no confidence it will all be recovered. Years down the road," he says wearily, "someone may end up with severe radiation poisoning because he's picked up a piece."

The telephone in Sigvaldason's office, which rings frequently, has the loud clatter of a fire alarm bell. After each brief conversation his concentration comes back quickly. He knows a great deal about Cosmos although nothing yet has been detected officially.

He enjoys taking frequent jabs at government. The hotel and taxi business was booming the first day Cosmos broke through the atmosphere. "The Russians have contributed more to the economy of the Yellowknife area in a few days than the Federal government does in a year."

58

The suggestion was made that Yellowknife Mayor Fred Henne should start a carnival while there was still plenty of excitement, and exploit the commercial possibilities of the accidental crash of Cosmos. Maybe Henne would even ask his Council to rename Yellowknife "Satellite City." At the same time the Mayor sent a testy telex to Barnett Danson, the Canadian Minister of Defense, protesting that no one had informed him of the possible danger of the landing. He assumed that Danson had advance information about the satellite and wanted an explanation for this off-handed treatment. His protests were ignored. The Minister was engaged on more important matters.

The reaction of Yellowknifers to Cosmos was light-hearted. They had already been through the arsenic poisoning scare a few years before when they felt all the government reports had been misleading. Arsenic seemed more real than a satellite from outer space. If they survived the arsenic hysteria, Henne thought, his citizens could deal with any emergency.

In a few days, the light-heartedness turned to indifference. Then talk started about radiation. Rumors spread about men in yellow suits from something called the Nuclear Accident Support Team. They had been seen at the airport hangars measuring radiation with odd-looking instruments. Some enterprising entrepreneur began selling T-shirts printed with a caricature of a Yellowknife raven astride Cosmos. They were a great commercial success. After a few days, life in Yellowknife continued pretty much as usual.

The Indian village of Detah across Yellowknife Bay from the town is easier to reach in winter than summer. In summer it's a dirty drive over a bad gravel road that takes you around the edge of the lake and comes to a dead end at the village, a collection of ramshackle wood houses on the top of a hill. In winter one drives over the ice road on the bay, which is cleared of snow by bulldozers to a width of about forty feet. On the blue ice a car careens perilously at high speed. Loads up to fifty tons can be carried safely over the four-foot-thick ice until the spring thaw cracks the mirror-flat surface with sharp, short explosions.

The Dog Rib Indians of Detah live in slum conditions. The twisting road through the village is piled high on either side with dirty mountains of snow. The good sled dogs are tied up and yelp from within the garages where the Indians tinker with their snowmobiles at all hours of the day. The old dogs slink over the roads, hunting in the garbage for scraps of food. The wood fires send up curls of thick smoke that hang like solid plumes of crystal in the blue sky. At the windows of the run-down frame houses, dark-faced children with streaming noses press against the frosted glass for a glimpse of strangers.

Once a week in winter the Dog Ribs go hunting, maybe for three days at a time, inspecting their trap lines for wolf or fox. They set up new traps and search for caribou, leaving their snowmobiles under a lean-to and proceeding with the dogs. Most of the year, however, the Dog Ribs collect social security payments and earn the unhealthy disrespect of the white towns-folk, who call them "welfare bums." Lethargy hangs over Detah as it does over most of the Indian villages. The lethargy is more like a smoldering form of resentment. The Dog Ribs take their handouts resentfully, knowing that their way of life is corrupt at the core. Except for a few of the young and one or two elders who serve on the North West Territory Council and speak for the village, the inhabitants are the product of half a century or more of slow debilitation, indifference, lassitude which have made them what they are today, a simple, naive people, superstitious, fearing change, frightened by events they do not understand. When Cosmos 954 flashed above them in a shattered fantail of blue flame it is little wonder that only Jimmy Doctor came forward to tell what he saw.

They are readily obedient to stern authority. One had to say to a Dog Rib, "Now, if you fish there you will be poisoned," or, "If you touch that you will die." That is the way the authorities believe you have to talk to the Indians. Thus they were quite understandably fearful of reporting what they had seen in the sky. A few years before they were told of fish in the Great Slave Lake being poisoned by arsenic from the mines. And now they were told that maybe what came out of the sky would poison them. The sea and the sky, the Dog Rib thought, were poisoning them. They didn't understand and did not wish to know.

In Detah village they go out to hunt in the morning before light. The villagers rise early. About the same time Marie Ruman comes back from cleaning her offices and Peter Pagonis delivers his containers of water to his customers and Johnny Doctor saw the prophecy realized. A meteor burning across the heavens above the Dog Ribs could only bring evil. It was a bad omen. If they said nothing and mused among themselves the evil thing that visited them from the heavens might go away. Perhaps it would not kill the caribou and musk ox and destroy their dogs.

Lifestyle of the north is easy. The wild embraces all strangers, soothes them and finally absorbs them. Distant from the happenings that dislocate communities in the south, a Yellowknifer feels isolated, divorced from elected government, baffled by a sense of ignorance about politics, environmentalists, Arctic reformers. He is weary of politicians who wanted to make their name by transforming the north into some kind of an example it was never meant to be. The north appeared unconquerable. It seemed to have inexhaustible wealth, an inability to be permanently maimed. People thought it could take endless abuse and exploitation because the land had some kind of eternal quality. Even the arsenic scare was no more than a minute tick scratching away at its mammoth, impervious hide. All this was true before Cosmos came.

Binx Remnant is a tall, chinless, sad-eyed man with a small head. Penetrating blue eyes and a warm, calm disposition make him immediately likeable. In every way he is the opposite of Sigvaldason. His character blends with the qualities of the land that dissolves man's impatience and pacifies his restlessness. Remnant was a traveling salesman fifteen years ago in the Northwest Territories. When he came to Yellowknife he stopped traveling. Now he is Clerk of the Legislative Assembly of the Northwest Territories, which has its sessions in the banquet room of the Explorer Hotel. Upstairs in one of the rooms Remnant conveniently has his office. There are fifteen members of the Legislative Assembly from all over the 1.5-million-square-mile territory.

Before Cosmos landed Remnant was busy organizing the Arctic Games to be held at Hay River, on the south shore of Great Slave Lake. Cosmos did not distract him very much. He often reflects on the remote nature of his life in the Territories. Excitement is not generated quickly among the native inhabitants – or within the impassive Remnant. The earth would have to open and swallow Yellowknife, he thinks, before the people would sit up and take notice. They don't become worked up very quickly. Remnant's unexcitable nasal drawl hardly alters in pitch as he speaks about his job as Clerk of the Assembly, or about the new Eskimo art collection to be housed in the partly constructed Yellowknife Museum. Like Sigvaldason, Remnant puffs on a briar pipe between sentences. He wants nothing to alter his way of life, including Cosmos. The Clerk enjoys his yearly camping holidays in the 2,000 square miles of protected preserve which includes the Thelon Game Sanctuary. Unfortunately the footprint of Cosmos runs right through the sanctuary, but Remnant was still unaware, like all Yellowknifers, of the extent of the radioactive contamination.

"Certainly," he said, "one would hope there is a minimum of damage. I'm not sure exactly what things like this can do. I don't know to what extent the radioactive pieces can be recovered. Are there many out there?" Remnant was at a loss to know what was happening. But he was not alone. The picture would remain unclear for a long time. Remnant wanted to go about his business undisturbed.

"I wouldn't say I am uninterested in the whole process. It would seem to me we are probably being looked after."

The Assembly, though elected, is controlled by a Commissioner responsible to the Minister of Northern Affairs. The huge deficit of the impossibly insolvent Northwest Territories administration is subsidized by the federal government. Little, if any, of the immense wealth removed from the territories remains in the area.

"I can't feel there's anything desperate to get concerned

about.'' Like Sigvaldason he couldn't understand why anyone would want to make a fuss about a satellite, parts of which had landed close by. The Arctic Games were a far more pressing matter.

Binx is a diligent Clerk of the Assembly. He keeps track of the members. The Indian member for Great Slave Lake is away at the moment hunting. He has also recently sold his trucking business and apparently has enjoyed his job on the Assembly so much it is now more or less his main occupation.

There are 47,000 people scattered over the 1.5 million square miles of Remnant's territory – about 30 people per square mile. But this proportion doesn't bother him. The population Remnant helps administer outside of Yellowknife are in tiny communities. They are trappers and hunters who follow the migration habits of the caribou in winter and keep close to their villages in other seasons. The few Royal Canadian Mounted Police are the only means the government has of keeping count of the native population and keeping law and order. The Mounties have their own aircraft and man the outposts up to the Arctic circle. Nurses and doctors pay periodic visits to the furthest and smallest settlements.

As far as military security is concerned, the north is the responsibility of the Canadian Forces Northern Command. Northern Command comes under the authority of Canadian Armed Forces Base, Edmonton – more commonly known as Namao, after the district in which it is located.

7

The Canadian Armed Forces Base at Namao spreads over 7,000 acres. The main part of the base is built around the air field with a 14,000-foot runway and, adjacent to it, a smaller one of 8,000 feet. It has a golf course, swimming pool and extensive recreational facilities for its 3,700 personnel. In World War II it was a staging base to move aircraft and supplies up from the USA to Alaska and the Aleutians. Normally 7,500 planes of all types arrive and depart weekly. In late January and February of 1978, this activity was quadrupled.

Ten miles away, in the oil-rich town of Edmonton, the new millionaires proudly display their Stetsons, cowboy boots and string bow ties. The older, more respectable money backs the recently built arts complex and other civic projects.

The heart of the Namao base is hangar five, where the transport squadrons are housed. The second floor of the hangar has become the headquarters for Operation Morning Light. It is a wide, high corridor, 150 yards long, with a number of rooms running off either side. On the stone floor of the hangar, five different squadrons have aircraft standing by in a state of readiness. The large-bodied c130 long-range Hercules aircraft from Squadron 435 supply army bases from the Northwest Territories all the way to Asia. The smaller, reliable Twin Otters are ideal for their role of flying mercy missions and rescue operations. The Otters are the workhorses of the north. During winter or summer they fly to every conceivable part of northern Canada. Each year they perform over 380 different tasks. It is not unusual for an Otter or Hercules to fly in $-80°$ weather to Arctic outposts.

On the second floor of hangar five is a glass case where

trophies and emblems of the squadron's past are proudly displayed. In the center is a gold-painted wooden lion, called "Chinthe," taken from a Buddhist temple in Burma during World War II. Over thirty-five years ago the men of squadron 435 were flying DC3 Dakotas over the Burma Pass, supplying the armies of the famous United States General Joseph Stillwell who helped organize the Chinese forces of Chiang Kai Shek in their fight against the Japanese. Squadron 435 in those distant, almost forgotten days played an illustrious role. The lion represents tradition for the pilots who today fly the transport planes out of Namao. This tradition gives a particular meaning to the new task the squadron was about to assume. Once again Squadron 435 was going onto active service.

Captain Delwood Huyghebaert is the adjutant of the Canadian Armed Forces Base at Edmonton. The descendant of Dutch Huguenots who settled in Ontario, he is a tubby, youthful man, fastidious in his ways and conscientious in the administration of his duties. For six years he flew C104 jets as part of the world-famous Canadian Aerobatic Team. But like every active pilot he was retired from fighter jets at a young age, before thirty.

Huyghebaert is not entirely at home in his job since his retirement from more active service, but he is slowly adapting. The first request he makes to strangers is to call him Yogi. He is fondly known as Yogi Bear and looks a little like him. Long ago his fellows stopped calling him by any other name.

Colonel David Garland, Commander of Base Edmonton, is fortunate in having Huyghebaert as his adjutant. Then, of course, there were many people who thought that the Canadians were lucky to have Garland at a time of national emergency when special qualities of leadership would be required. General Gates said of him, "Garland was probably one of the best officers I have ever known." And Gates is not a man given to many compliments. But Garland would not be the personality he is, nor would Gates' compliment be significant, without taking into account the highly professional force of pilots, engineers and technicians that serve under his command. They form part of one of the best-trained small professional armies in the world. They are among the highest paid of servicemen anywhere and have excellent morale. Garland comes from Newfoundland, a terrain as rugged and wild as the one he oversees.

When Troy Wade, the deputy manager of NEVOO, was notified on January 24 in Las Vegas that the NEST team were going to Namao, he was told the on-scene commander would be Garland. Wade telephoned him immediately. He had been ready to go somewhere since Monday, January 23, but he didn't know where. Now he did. That is, he knew from a map that he was going to northern Canada; but the idea was as unreal as the entire operation had been to date. He had never been to Canada before.

The three loaded and fully equipped C141 jets were ready at their bases in various parts of the United States. As Gates told the Defense Minister Barnett Danson when they met in Edmonton, these three aircraft carried the entire US capability. Danson observed the three C141s with their mobile communication trucks, helicopters, aluminum containers stuffed with data processing equipment, a staff of 113 American scientists, technicians and secretaries and shook his head in some disbelief. If anything had happened to the three jet transports it would have been a major catastrophe.

Wade had undergone three harrowing, sleepless days prior to his phone call to Garland. His phone had rung incessantly as the reports on Cosmos flowed in. There were a couple of frightening hours in the early morning of January 24 when Cosmos vanished on all the radar systems of the western world. But Wade was given the general area of the landing by the time Garland had been contacted.

President Jimmy Carter had been in touch with Canadian Prime Minister Pierre Trudeau. And Ivan Prior, the Prime Minister's special assistant, had already held lengthy conversations with the United States Security Advisor, Zbigniew Brzezinski. Everything was laid on – everything, that is, except the exact size, mission and location of the satellite.

66

It was fortunate that Garland, as the operational chief of Morning Light, was a good organizational man. The politicians might make policy decisions but they were ignorant of the magnitude of the problem. Garland was not. He knew how difficult it was, even in summer, to search for a single human being lost in the Canadian wilderness who might be alive and capable of actively signaling his whereabouts. Now it was dead winter. The coldest months of the year were ahead and he had to look for pieces of metal – not one but dozens, maybe thousands. He was aware that the metal would be radioactive and there were instruments to detect radioactivity. The base had its own Nuclear Accident Support Team for radioactive emergencies, but they could not begin to cope with what lay ahead. The Canadian Atomic Energy Control Board (AECB) had sent Roger Eaton, a PhD in physical chemistry, to represent them at Namao.

The Geological Survey of Canada, a branch of the Department of Energy, Mines and Resources, flew up a small contingent consisting, among others, of Keith Richardson, Robert Grasty and Quentin Bristow. The two first men were PhDs in their chosen fields of geology and long experienced in natural uranium surveys in the north. The third, Bristow, was an engineer of unusual talent. They were all to play a vital role in Operation Morning Light.

David Garland did not know what to expect from the Americans. He had no idea of their equipment, their number, their ability or their background. But he did know that the Canadians were insufficiently equipped to mount a search operation of their own on the scale required. Besides, time was of the essence. The more trained men and equipment that were available the easier it would be for Garland to do his job. He would welcome whatever assistance he could get.

Meanwhile, Garland was very busy. He was not a man to waste time, and orders of the day went out announcing Operation Morning Light. His lieutenant Colonels of the Northern Command – men like William Butchart, Donald Davidson and Alex Bialosh – were given their assignments.

The pilots of the search and rescue teams were ready. Everyone of importance would be on twenty-four-hour call. Several rooms on the second floor of hangar five were cleared and made ready for the arrival of the Americans. Wade had told Garland on January 24 that he would be leaving Las Vegas at 1:15 PM local time and hoped to be at Namao before 6:00 that evening. His men would be prepared to transfer all equipment to the Canadian C130 Hercules and would be operational two hours later. From army stores Garland ordered Arctic suits for the personnel who would be part of the US search team. These suits consisted of nylon outer boots with an inner fur-lined one, woolen caps, special padded gloves laced by a long string that went behind the neck so they could be removed and not lost, a quilted army parka and trousers. A man dressed in such an outfit would keep from freezing to death even if he was forced down in a plane in $-50°$ weather. The 14,000-foot runway at Namao was kept clear to receive the huge C141 jets flying up from their bases in the south.

Not only was Garland in command, but he would assert that command in a manner that expedited the work of everyone. He had already drawn a large organizational chart detailing the chain of command in Operation Morning Light and placed it on the wall in the operations room. He wanted everyone to know his job from the outset. At the top of the chart was Garland, the undisputed on-scene commander. His second in command was Lieutenant Colonel Bialosh, his major Canadian scientific advisors Roger Eaton and Keith Richardson. On the US side, Mahlon Gates was chief from DOE, his assistant Troy Wade and his scientific advisor Richard Wagner. John Doyle was in charge of all US equipment. From these key personnel the lines of communication spread to a large array of scientists and technicians responsible for various areas of data gathering and analysis. The Canadian military controlled the planes and the means of carrying out the job. A "Mission Planning Group" under Garland would unify the different tasks of Canadian and American personnel, and Garland had responsibility for integrating everything. On the sides of the wall chart were written

68

the objectives of Operation Morning Light. The Department of National Defense was "to locate, secure and identify risk." The Atomic Energy Control Board was to "recover, store and dispose."

On another wall, a huge map divided the satellite's footprint into segments thirty miles wide and fifty long from Yellowknife to Baker Lake. This footprint ran in a northeast direction.

When Troy Wade arrived with his team he was surprised at the expertly coordinated set up. He had never worked with Canadians before, and he had no idea what to expect. Neither did the Canadians.

The Americans had come to Canada not only with their complete technical operation but also with their public relations apparatus. This was in the form of Dave Jackson, head of public relations at the Las Vegas office. The United States Department of Energy was ultra-sensitive to all information that affected NEST. It did not like to release stories unless it supervised their contents; a representative sat in on interviews with their members. In Canada, Jackson was operating, as far as security was concerned, in a foreign country. No foreign country was easily permitted to look into secrets linked with the United States defense effort.

For a few days nobody knew who was responsible for the official releases which were all the worried Canadian public had for information. The Canadian public relations team, which consisted of Lieutenant Colonel Beverley Totman and Major Victor Keating, was comparatively inexperienced in the ways of the world media. But there weren't many public relations men who could cope with the avalanche of international reporters and television companies who descended by the hundreds into the ground floor briefing room of hangar five. Garland found it necessary to print his biography to save him from endless repetition. To a large extent Jackson, a reporter by training, found himself very much in his element as the public relations man behind the scenes, responsible for most of the news releases. Jackson had a considerable knowledge of all the technical procedures in quite astonishing detail. He could explain any operation, give the technical background and parry the bombardment of international press questions with practiced skill. He oversaw a large office in Las Vegas which functioned on a twenty-four-hour basis. His job was to explain nuclear accidents, explosions on the Test Site and related subjects in a manner which would reflect well on the Department of Energy. Also, in Las Vegas (as in all other United States institutions connected with nuclear development) there was a thick curtain of secrecy. A man could only say to the public part of what he knew and Jackson was there to make sure this happened.

While this policy could work well in the tight, insulated, security-conscious institutions of the United States, Canada represented quite another situation. Here things were much more open. Normally it would have been impossible to see the entire NEST group together, or to have such a close look at the methods they employed.

Even though the Canadians had a few secrets of their own, Defense Minister Danson decided at the beginning that everything would be disclosed. There would be nothing withheld from the anxious public. The Americans were not prepared for this kind of open operation, but they had been instructed to remain in the background. They were guests in a foreign country. All the press knew officially was that there were a number of United States scientists available to assist the Canadians. But the Americans were well briefed from the beginning. They were courteous and reserved. But Jackson was by nature a high-powered man and he had much difficulty remaining subdued for long.

The Americans kept out of sight as much as they could. But they were easy to identify in Yellowknife at the Explorer Hotel, in the operational rooms at hangar five and the headquarters of Northern Command. They possessed most of the equipment and men. They also had plenty of backup facilities. For every man of NEST in Canada there were half a dozen more back in California or New Mexico or Nevada who were working on some piece of equipment which, with a phone call, could be sent on the next flight to Edmonton. The Canadians had about a dozen scientists and technicians on the job.

The NEST team were not only in Canada because of a presidential directive, but more than likely because they also knew they would be gaining invaluable experience of a magnitude never envisaged in peace time. The territory where Cosmos landed would be a perfect location to exercise the complete United States capability. But while the search teams were reasonably prepared for the radiation danger, no one was ready for the overwhelming world interest. Even Jackson – long accustomed to constant phone calls and television appearances – could not cope with the deluge that almost drowned the public relations men at Namao. The media came from the United States, Japan and Australia, every major European capital and just about everywhere in Canada. The only western newspaper that didn't give the event sensational coverage was Sig Sigvaldason's *Yellowknifer,* circulation not advertised.

8

On the morning of January 25, a high-flying United States military U2 jet surveyed the projected footprint from Yellowknife to Baker Lake. Jets sampled air as far away as Michigan. But there were no positive results. Since no nuclear fallout from the enriched uranium core of Cosmos had been detected at high altitude it was possible the core debris or the entire core itself, was embedded somewhere in the snow or ice of the footprint.

At 7:30 AM on the same day, three Canadian Hercules C130 propeller-driven aircraft had taken off from the long runway at Namao. Each plane was equipped with a gamma ray spectrometer, which could measure radioactivity on the ground along their flight path. The aim was to investigate the entire reentry area in one quick sweep. If the core was on the ground there should be a violent response on the gamma ray spectrometers. Two of the instruments had been transferred the night before from the US C141 transports, the third had been built by Quentin Bristow of the Canadian Geological Survey. All were sensitive enough to detect any man-made radiation.

However, a complication soon developed. The flight plan carried the Hercules over many outcroppings of rocks that were rich in natural uranium deposits. While the charts that were recorded by the spectrometers might have been invaluable to uranium prospectors they were of no use to the hunters of Cosmos. The magnetic tapes from the American detectors had to be removed after the flight and interpreted by the data processing machines. Only then could they tell the difference between radiation emitted from man-made sources and natural deposits.

For two days twelve aircraft searched desperately for some

sign of the highly radioactive satellite core or, for that matter, any piece of the debris that would confirm the presence of Cosmos. Without some fragment there would be no proof that the Russian satellite had actually landed. The mammoth effort being expended by two nations would be in vain. Something had to be found quickly to provide the tangible evidence the world awaited.

The three C130s flew at an altitude of 1,000 feet up and down the footprint along predetermined grid lines. On either side cruised three CC138 Twin Otters. Below the fixed-wing aircraft hovered one enormous CH147 heavy-lift Chinook helicopter, and dancing just above the trees were the smaller three CC135 Twin Huey helicopters. Not far off was the one DOE Convair with infrared equipment. On each plane, in addition to the pilots and flight engineers, the scientists and technicians, there was a single Canadian Forces corporal. This man was an expert at survival in the arctic cold. As long as the flight went smoothly he had no specific responsibilities. But if the plane went down, his job was to keep everyone on it alive. Though low in rank, in an emergency the corporal would outrank everyone.

Few of these men had slept more than a couple of hours during the preceding two days. The excitement was so great, the atmosphere so tense, that exhaustion had not yet set in. Colonel Garland was beginning to have serious doubt they would find anything. Bell and Morrison checked and rechecked their calculations with some trepidation. Maybe they had made a mistake. Below the low-flying aircraft the clear white snowscape was unblemished by any sign of Cosmos. Doubt was openly expressed. The news-starved media felt their frenzied invasion of the north had been premature. The authorities in Ottawa and Washington began to suspect that there was nothing to find. The satellite had burned up on reentry. Eyewitness accounts could not be relied upon for accuracy.

Back in hangar five the forty-eight NAST members stood by in their yellow suits and gas masks. Their job was to check personnel who had come in contact with Cosmos debris for contamination. If necessary, they could be sent into the field.

They carried standard pencil-size dosimeters and X-ray film strips in their lapels to monitor their own level of contamination should they come in contact with radioactive material.

Once the hit was made and located the scientists of the Canadian AECB would have the responsibility of physically retrieving and placing the pieces of Cosmos into special lead containers to be shipped back to Canada's Whiteshell Atomic Energy Laboratory near Winnipeg for analysis. The organization everywhere was good. The search teams were immensely eager to make that first hit. But nothing was happening. The press and television were seeking morsels of news; anything that sounded like good drama became a story, anybody that sounded authoritative was quoted. But there was still little solid information.

On the morning of January 28, a Canadian Hercules carrying Quentin Bristow's gamma ray spectrometer was flying over the western end of the footprint when the pen that records ground radiation on a chart made several sudden jagged lines. They were markedly different from the regular series of small troughs and crests. A hit had been made. There could be no doubt about it: Bristow's spectrometer had detected the first evidence of man-made radiation. The navigator informed Bristow that they were in the McLeod Bay region, north of Fort Reliance at the northeast end of Great Slave Lake.

Quentin Bristow is a short, modest man, a native Englishman who has both a sense of humor and a sense of history. He designed and built his gamma ray spectrometer over the period of a year, working on it whenever he could spare time from his other duties. By coincidence, he finished it only a few days before Cosmos came down. Because he classified it as an experimental machine he put "a few extra bells and whistles on it." Bristow knew that the Americans were just as capable of building such an instrument (which combined a detector with a minicomputer), but their requirements were different. They were more concerned with detecting radiation leaks from man-made

74

sources, and therefore needed a mobile spectrometer which they could fit into small, maneuverable helicopters. The magnetic tapes that recorded findings could be read later.

Since the Canadians usually searched for natural uranium sources from a larger aircraft, the size of the spectrometer was not a problem. So Bristow's machine was big: ten feet long, five feet high and three feet wide. The mini-computer incorporated into it could translate results immediately and thereby save a good deal of time. This was the reason that Bristow received a call on January 26 from the search team, asking him to fly up immediately with his instrument. His ingenious spectrometer made a tremendous difference during those first few days, when there were few facts, much speculation and much doubt about the outcome of the search. It became a legitimate source of pride for the Canadians, who were always sensitive to the wealth, the might, and the generous commitment of the US forces.

Bristow vividly recalls the hours leading up to that moment of discovery on the Hercules. He will probably never forget them. It was only some thirty-six hours before, at 10:00 PM on January 26, that he had boarded a plane waiting for him and his machine at Uplands airport near Ottawa. From the moment that he strapped himself in, after considerable heaving and pushing to get the cumbersome spectrometer on board, Bristow was caught up completely in the feverish excitement of the mission. At 2:00 the next morning he arrived at Namao, removed and checked over his equipment and immediately transferred it into the big belly of a waiting Hercules. Instead of taking a few hours' needed rest, Bristow, in a slight daze, accepted an invitation to go out flying. Four hours later, at 6:00 AM Friday, January 27, he flew off in the Hercules. For twelve hours he remained aloft, monitoring the spectrometer. When he returned to base he felt more dead than alive and immediately went to bed.

Another group of scientists, including Bristow's colleagues Robert Grasty and Peter Holman, immediately climbed aboard the Hercules and prepared to do a further twelve-hour search.

They concentrated largely on the area around the eastern end of Great Slave Lake and a number of press people accompanied them. This was the beginning of the third day of the hunt for Cosmos and doubts were growing about whether they would really discover any radioactive debris. Grasty, Holman and the weary press contingent returned from their twelve-hour shift at 6:00 AM. Soon afterwards, Bristow prepared to climb back on board for another turn. He felt refreshed after his sleep, even though he had been awakened by thoughts of some new computer programs he wanted to write for the search operations.

Before Grasty and Holman left the plane they quietly examined the chart run out by the mini-computer and showed it to Bristow. They all saw an enormous "blip" on the chart, and knew they had located a piece of Cosmos. At the time of the hit they had been flying over lake ice, where there could be no natural radioactivity. Grasty, Holman and Bristow were jubilant, but their jubilation was tempered by caution. They had found the first indisputable evidence of a man-made object that emitted strong gamma rays. Now, however, the object had to be relocated on the ground.

This was much more difficult than merely discovering the radiation. In those early flights the planes had to navigate by a system called the Omega satellite system. Normally this is fine for flights where a mile or less of accuracy is required. But to relocate tiny pieces of metal the search team would have to navigate to within yards of the objective. The hit made by the spectrometer had to be identified with the correct geographical coordinates on the ground so that the helicopters could land and the debris be removed.

This proved, for the moment, to be impossible: Thane Hendricks, the American computer expert who examined the magnetic tape from Bristow's spectrometer (which had recorded the hit) couldn't read it. He didn't know the formula, and Bristow, the only man who did, was back on the Hercules for another twelve-hour shift. Hendricks might eventually have learned the formula himself, but it would take hours. He decided to wait for Bristow to return.

76

An important discovery had been made but only one man could, for the time being, assess its true significance. This was an odd situation: the mighty efforts of two nations awaited the return of a single scientist to determine whether their enormous commitment had been justified. Without definite proof that Cosmos was somewhere on the ground, there was no point to the entire search. That first hit would provide the proof, the incentive, the drive for the teams of men to carry on their work.

Thus, when Bristow returned and wearily clambered out of the Hercules, Hendricks was waiting for him. The first words he said were, "What's the code?" Once Bristow had told Hendricks the code the tape was read off and the nature of the large blip on the chart properly interpreted. It was obvious to all the scientists that one large spike on the graph had to be man-made. This was the major breakthrough.

In the end it was of no importance who would be the first to prove the physical remains of Cosmos were actually lying on the Barrens. But all the same, the tired Bristow felt a little twinge of pride in his achievement, although he had some misgivings. Like all Canadians he would have been just as happy if there had been nothing to find. But this would have been hoping for too much.

"We now had the first piece of evidence that anybody had, that anything had landed," Bristow said. "It was bad news. Where something had landed we knew there had to be more."

Although the press had been on the flight when the discovery was made, they had no idea what Bristow's spectrometer was doing or how it operated. A small blip on a chart meant nothing to them. It looked like their own electrocardiograms. No one went out of their way to advertise the news. Grasty kept the secret from the public relations people as long as he could. But it was difficult to keep a secret for long from Dave Jackson. It was not until some hours later that word filtered down from the Operation Room that a piece of radioactive, man-made debris had been found. "The press," Bristow said, "descended from every direction." He hadn't realized that so many press agencies, magazines and television stations existed. "I have

77

never seen such a circus," he said. Bristow, who is retiring and
reticent, didn't understand what the fuss was about. All his
machine had done was to register a hit on a radioactive fragment.
But he now held the world stage. He handled it all quite calmly,
unperturbed by the attention. Bristow was interviewed, photographed, quoted and sucked dry of every ounce of information
by the news-hungry media. The engineer was rather amused by
this new experience as a celebrity, which contrasted markedly to
the anonymous life of a civil servant which he normally enjoyed.

Later, when the "circus" was over and the fuss died away,
Bristow took off some time to write a new computer program
and add a few refinements, such as an instant heat detection
analyzer. He could not help deriving pleasure from the success
of his machine. Bristow was not a Canadian chauvinist, but
undoubtedly between him and Grasty there must have been
smug, unexpressed joy at the achievement. Of course, Bristow
was too sensible to believe he had done anything so remarkable
that it was beyond the reach of his American colleagues. The
Canadians had long experience in this rough country, but not in
winter. The Americans had only been in these hostile conditions
a few days. They had almost without exception come from a
southern, hospitable environment. When the Americans went
into full gear with their immense back-up resources, there was
very little in the world that would be able to equal them. The
motive of competition, of sensitive pride where the Americans
were concerned, was all one-sided. Canadians are traditionally
apt to have some acute feelings in these matters. However, this
was an emergency and the clear-headed Garland and his team
appreciated the assistance. The American scientists and technicians stayed out of sight in spite of the urgings of their public
relations man, allowing the Canadian scientists and military to
make all the announcements. They would have their turn when
they returned home. But no American was really prepared for
what he saw on the Barrens. And this included Joe Tinney, the
scientist from Livermore, who had worked on Project Crested
Ice in Greenland ten years before.

Bristow would work without interruption on Operation

Morning Light until February 26. Then he would return home for a few days to replace the three pairs of socks and two shirts he had brought with him. As he said, the twelve-hour shifts "were getting a bit much."

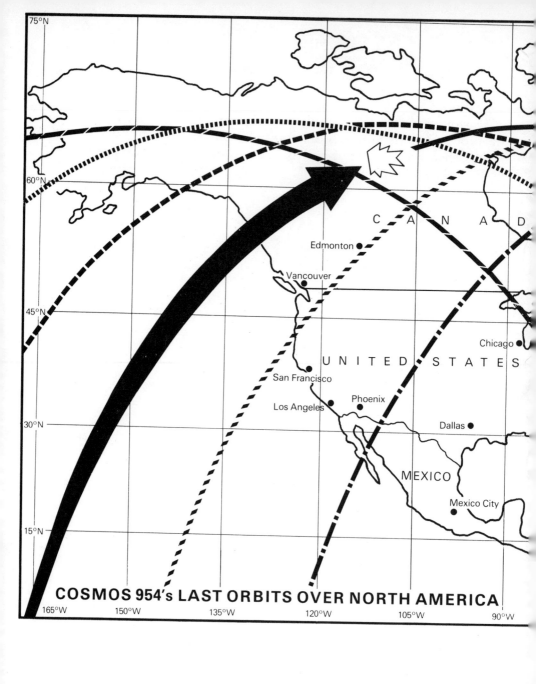

COSMOS 954's LAST ORBITS OVER NORTH AMERICA

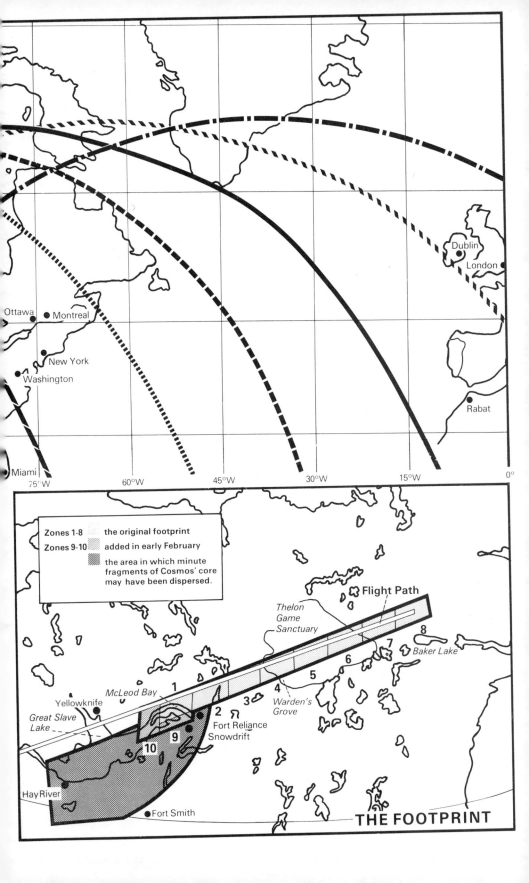

Dublin
London

Ottawa ● Montreal

New York
Washington

Miami
75°W   60°W   45°W   30°W   15°W   0°

Rabat

Zones 1-8   the original footprint
Zones 9-10   added in early February
             the area in which minute
             fragments of Cosmos' core
             may have been dispersed.

⟨⟩ Flight Path

Thelon
Game
Sanctuary

8

7
Baker Lake

6

5

McLeod Bay   1

Yellowknife   4   Warden's
                    3   Grove
Great Slave   2
Lake   Fort Reliance
             9   Snowdrift
         10

Hay River

● Fort Smith

THE FOOTPRINT

ABOVE A view of Yellow-
knife. *Department of
National Defense.*

RIGHT Sig Sigvaldason
outside the offices of his
newspaper, the *Yellow-
knifer.*

ABOVE Members of the
Canadian Nuclear Accident
Search Team (NAST) in full
dress. *Department of
National Defense*

ABOVE In the foreground, a Canadian Hercules. In the background, the three C 141s carrying "the total US capability" for dealing with nuclear accidents. *Department of National Defense.*

BELOW A baby American helicopter being loaded into a Canadian Hercules within hours after Cosmos' crash. The helicopter would operate from the body of the mother ship. *Department of National Defense.*

ARMED FORCES

ABOVE A Canadian Twin Otter that has just landed on the ice at the eastern end of Great Slave Lake. Special landing techniques were required to keep friction created by the plane's aluminum skis from melting the ice.

BELOW Scientists and technicians aboard a DOE Convair with infrared sensing equipment and aerial cameras. *EG&G*.

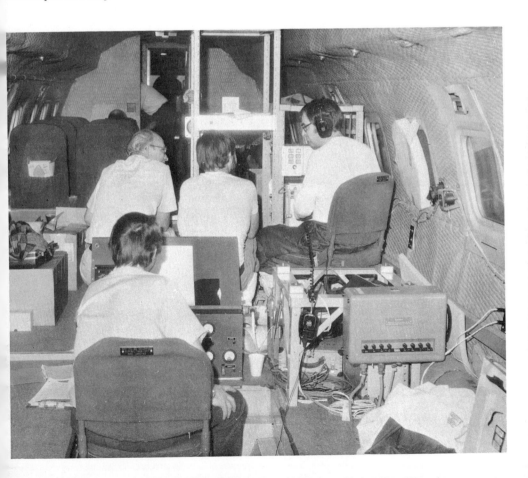

OPPOSITE Inside a Hercules aircraft: the machine is Quentin Bristow's gamma ray spectrometer. *Department of National Defense.*

BELOW A closeup view of Bristow's spectrometer. *Department of National Defense.*

BOTTOM An example of a Low Altitude Parachute Extraction System (LAPES) drop. Flying a few feet above the ground, a Hercules releases parachutes which in turn pull out the cargo – in this case, a bulldozer. *Department of National Defense.*

BELOW An aerial view of Camp Garland. The hangars and living quarters were all made of tents specially built to withstand Arctic conditions. *Department of National Defense.*

RIGHT Opening day at Camp Garland. US and Canadian personnel posed together for this photograph. *Department of National Defense.*

LEFT The flags flying at Camp Garland. Below the US flag is the California bear of Lawrence Livermore Laboratory. This flag had been displayed in the Aleutians, Colorado, and Wyoming before making its appearance at Camp Garland. *EG&G.*

BELOW A curious hunter stops with his team of huskies at Camp Garland. *Department of National Defense.*

ABOVE A campsite at the eastern end of Great Slave Lake. In the background a Twin Huey helicopter is preparing to take off. *Department of National Defense.*

BELOW Another camp on Great Slave Lake. The Chinook helicopter in the background has just brought equipment from Yellowknife. *EG&G.*

ABOVE A helicopter landing in typical wilderness terrain for close inspection of a hit. *Department of National Defense.*

BELOW Searchers investigating a piece of Cosmos debris. Hand-held gamma ray spectrometers revealed that the pieces were not radioactive. *Department of National Defense.*

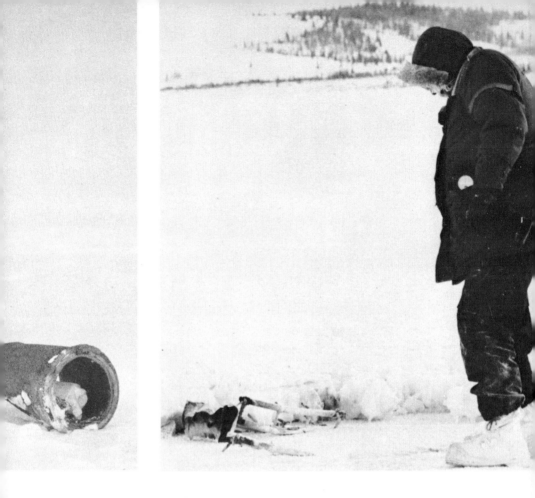

ABOVE LEFT A searcher
cautiously approaches some
fragments with his hand-
held spectrometer. *EG&G*.

LEFT Another piece of
debris. This one is radioactive, and has been marked
off with bunting. It will be
removed shortly. *EG&G*.

ABOVE RIGHT Part of the
Cosmos debris accidentally
discovered by two
adventurers as they passed
the site with their dog team.
EG&G.

RIGHT A small fragment
being checked again for its
radioactivity reading. The
reading is very low here –
otherwise no one would
dare come so close to it.

ABOVE At the eastern end of
Great Slave Lake, a
recovery crew prepares to
remove a source buried
under the snow.

ABOVE A typical landing on Great Slave Lake in late January. The temperature is −70°. *EG&G.*

Ice and water samples being taken from a lake. They will be tested for radioactivity. *EG&G.*

ABOVE, TOP Cleaning up a radioactive site on Great Slave Lake. *EG&G.*

ABOVE Radioactive debris being lowered into a canister. *Department of National Defense.*

ABOVE A Canadian cleanup team at work: Pat Cahill is wielding the shovel while Ross Brown stands by on the right. In the distance stands the village of Snowdrift.

BELOW Brown (facing camera) and Cahill check the radioactivity of the snow they are packing away for removal from Great Slave Lake. On the left is an RCMP constable.

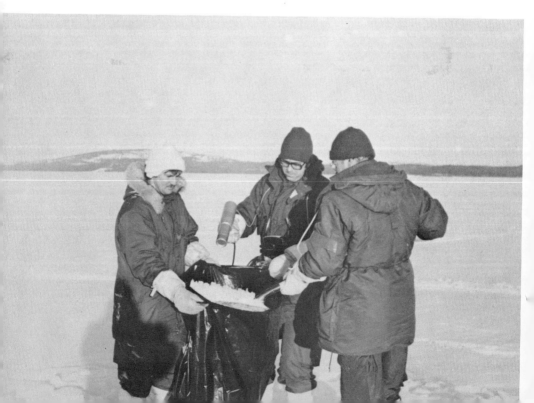

ABOVE Packing up the
contaminated snow.
Eventually this practise had
to be abandoned because
of the sheer quantity of
radioactive particles on
Great Slave Lake.

BELOW Ross Brown
trekking across Great Slave
Lake in search of debris.

ABOVE The constable
driving back to the airplane
with a container holding
radioactive material.

ABOVE The author on
Great Slave Lake.

RIGHT Ross Brown back at
the plane. Hooked to his
belt is the gamma ray
spectrometer he always
carried; in front of him, a
container full of
contaminated material.

ABOVE The man who has just gotten off the snowmobile is Bill Liechtmeijer, the RCMP constable whose job it was to keep Chipewyan indians away from the radioactive debris cordoned off near Snowdrift. Here he is meeting the search team at their Twin Otter airplane.

BELOW Canadian Armed Forces personnel camping in the wilderness near Snowdrift. At night the temperature averages about −60°, not counting wind chill.

LEFT, TOP The decontamination area inside the Canadian Forces hangar at Yellowknife. The men in protective garments are members of the Canadian NAST. *Department of National Defense.*

LEFT, BOTTOM A downed Chinook helicopter at Fort Reliance. Long hours took their toll on man and machine alike.

BELOW Investigating the mysterious crater at Cape Dorset: the man here is sawing through five-foot-thick ice to take samples. The badge on his lapel will register any radiation present at the site. *Department of National Defense.*

ABOVE Drilling into the ice
at Cape Dorset. The shorter
man facing the camera is a
local Eskimo. *Department
of National Defense.*

RIGHT Some of the heavy
equipment used at the Cape
Dorset site. *Department of
National Defense.*

OPPOSITE Inheritors of the
nuclear age: children in one
of the small communities
near Great Slave Lake being
checked for radioactive
contamination. *Department
of National Defense.*

9

The Egerton, Grier and Germanhausen research laboratory at
Santa Barbara, California, fits comfortably into its surroundings
of shrubbery, clipped lawns and shading palm trees whose
fronds rustle slowly in the peaceful breeze from the Pacific
Ocean. The setting has a feeling of relaxed detachment.

In a second-floor office of the EG&G building, Richard Lynn,
wearing an open-necked shirt and casual sportswear, sometimes
sits dictating letters to Pat Styer, his fastidious secretary. She
keeps a close account of all Lynn's movements, and always
knows where to find him day or night. He leaves a careful
itinerary behind so he can always be reached. Lynn's wife is
a doctor. They have three children and live in Santa Barbara's
suburbs, enjoying all the rewards that a highly paid research
scientist receives.

When Lynn is not in his office he is down in the laboratory
working on experiments, usually concerned these days with
improving methods of radiation detection. He has been working
on these and related problems for ten years. Lynn is the assistant program manager at the laboratory under Harold
Lommonds. Among the NEST group, he seems to have the widest
range of interests. He has traveled the most for pleasure and
knowledge, and finds time to read about subjects other than
scientific. He appears more interested than many of his colleagues in the cultural life that surrounds him in the urbane
community of Santa Barbara.

Lynn is a man of medium height and dark features. He has
black, curly hair, wears glasses and possesses a reticent, somewhat sensitive disposition. He is a careful man. Cooperative
and friendly, he talks openly up to a point; but he knows where

to stop when he reaches the security barrier. He shows a greater flexibility than most of his colleagues, and seems somehow to possess more compassion, though he is not anxious to display it.

Lynn's highly specialized field of research, which is sponsored by the Department of Energy, is part of a long-range program called SANDS (Surveillance Accident Nuclear Detection System). At present he is working on special material development, and is particularly concerned with mercury crystals. He hopes this will be an improvement on potassium iodide, which is the basis of all gamma ray spectrometers. Potassium iodide has certain disadvantages: the crystals can crack in very cold weather conditions. This has become an important problem in the two largest operations where gamma ray spectrometry has played a role: Crested Ice and Morning Light. Both have taken place in sub-zero temperatures.

Since Lynn first joined NEST in 1973, his work has taken him around the world a great deal. Prolonged absences are something that the families of NEST members learn to live with. No member has ever been known to refuse an assignment for personal reasons.

Dick Lynn's piercing dark eyes seem to cloud over when he is puzzled or disturbed by the intent of a question. He has long since acquired the knack of directing conversation into other channels when it threatens to enter forbidden areas. He tries to reduce all things to their simplest form: in an environment where sophisticated machines and government organizations are multitudinous, and multiplying all the time, initials become second nature. For a stranger, they are bewildering. Like other NEST members, Lynn steers away from comment about politics, or about his superiors at DOE. He has all the makings of an ideal civil servant – though he probably doesn't realize it. He does not fit entirely into the NEST mold, but he has the same sense of pride and motivation, and at times must be tempted by the comforts of conformity. His specialized scientific knowledge makes him an essential member of the team.

At the beginning Lynn believed he would not participate in Operation Morning Light. He first heard the news of Cosmos' reentry at 10:30 AM on January 24, when he received a call from Robert Durkee in Las Vegas. Although Las Vegas NEST was on the alert and would shortly be deployed to Edmonton there was only limited space in the C141 and no immediate need to send the Santa Barbara contingent. Lynn was a little disappointed at the news but somehow felt he had not heard the last of the matter. That same day he left for Florida with one of his associates, an electronics engineer named Jack Guerrier, on some other business.

Next morning, over breakfast at the Holiday Inn in Cocoa Beach, Lynn looked at the front page of the *Miami Herald*. The large headlines dealt with the breakup and reentry of Cosmos. Northern Canada and the Great Slave Lake seemed very far away from Cocoa Beach. As he and Jack Guerrier sat over their coffee they talked about the Cosmos project and tried to visualize some of the difficulties facing the men who would be going to Canada. In the afternoon, when their business was through, they left for Orlando International Airport to catch a flight out.

While lunching in the airport restaurant, Lynn suddenly heard his name being paged over the loudspeaker. He hurried to take a telephone call that was waiting for him. His secretary was urgently phoning from California. She told Lynn that a message had been sent to him from Namao: a microprocessor-based data-acquisition system was required immediately. This unit had the capability for storing and comparing the results from different readings given out on the gamma ray spectrometers being used by the search team. It would be able to differentiate between small, man-made debris and natural background radiation, and would therefore be enormously useful for the men at Namao. The machine was small enough to fit into a briefcase, so shipping it would be no problem; but it had to be modified in various ways for the conditions of the north.

Lynn was the man to supervise these modifications. He hung up the phone, sat down with Guerrier, and discussed the problem over the remainder of lunch. Half an hour later he called Frank Urrico, head of the engineer support section at EG&G in Santa Barbara, and gave him some preliminary instructions. Then he went back to the restaurant, where Guerrier was already doing some calculations.

By 2 PM Guerrier had the solution to the problem clear in his mind. He went to the airport telephone, called EG&G in Santa Barbara, and suggested the modifications that should be made before he and Lynn arrived that night. Guerrier said that he would rewrite the computer programs himself but this could only be done if the changes were already made. Half an hour before their flight departed for Los Angeles, Lynn managed to remove his briefcase microprocessor from the freight office and carried it with him on the plane as hand luggage. He wanted to make sure the machine was safe and within easy reach. On the Florida assignment it had been used successfully; in Canada it could supplement the one whose wire circuitry they were already modifying in the laboratory at Santa Barbara.

Shortly after 10 PM that night the two weary men showed up at the Santa Barbara laboratory. Urrico was waiting. Without delay Guerrier started on the modifications. Then Lynn called the NEST number at Namao and to his surprise General Gates answered the phone. Gates passed the call to John Doyle, who was responsible for all the equipment. For a while the two men discussed the complexity of the problem. Operating in the bitter cold of the Barrens presented difficulties no one anticipated. Wires became brittle and snapped. Batteries went dead and unless your hands were gloved, frostbite occurred within minutes and operation of the equipment became impossible. Lynn listened with awe and respect as Doyle discussed the problems. He would not forget the advice he received. At 2 AM he went home for a few hours of sleep while Guerrier worked all through the night. At 7 AM he was back at the laboratory again to do some testing on the AGA sodium iodide detector and the AGA portable infrared scanning system, both of which he had been asked to bring along with him. He still had plenty of testing and adapting to do – maybe six to eight hours if all went well.

It was now January 26 and the modifications were taking

longer than Lynn and Guerrier had expected. Their flight to Edmonton was postponed from that evening to the next morning at 7:00 AM. Technicians and engineers were working around the clock. In the afternoon Lynn drove around his old car to the laboratory so they could load on the equipment that night. There were no trucks available for rent, and the suitcases of equipment and instruments were piling up. When they departed, the small Californian-Mexican Benny Lopez, who was to accompany them, would somehow have to find room to squeeze in amidst the mass of machinery. About midnight everything was packed and the men were set to leave for Los Angeles so they could catch their flight early the next morning. It was a 250-mile drive. But Lynn had trouble starting his old vehicle. He finally succeeded after tinkering with the solenoid and the group began to drive south. At 4:00 AM the trio arrived at the airport and sat around the terminal, dozing and talking, until their 7:00 AM flight. The Western Airlines flight made four stops on the way but the men were too groggy to notice.

When they got to customs at Edmonton, the Canadian official took one look at the strange equipment and invited the unshaven scientists into his private office for a chat. He asked Lynn what he intended to do with all the apparatus. Lynn did his best to explain, but he was haggard from lack of rest and had not foreseen this particular difficulty. He showed the customs man his special identity card. Then the official made a telephone call, and suddenly everything was understood. The scientists were ushered quickly through customs and the official wished them all good luck on their mission. Lynn rented a truck at the airport and without further delay they transferred their instruments and drove to a nearby hotel.

From there, Lynn called Namao and was told they had to report to base within three hours. It was now 5:30 PM. At 8:30 PM the men were in the operations center being briefed. The briefings continued until 4 AM the following morning. After that Lynn and Guerrier returned to the hotel for six hours of sleep. For Jack Guerrier, it was the first time he had been to bed in three days.

10

Three days had passed. Nothing of major importance had been sighted and the only fragments retrieved were small. One false alarm had been raised but speedily attributed to a machine malfunction. In some quarters it was seriously and openly being stated that there would be little debris to recover. Captain Caesar Jordaens of Northern Command believed that the satellite had almost completely burnt up in space.

But Operation Morning Light went on day and night. Every man and every piece of machinery available in North America were devoted to the task. The experts were doing their best, but when that didn't produce results they were bound to be criticized by the skeptics.

One Yellowknife resident claimed to have spotted three Russians moving clandestinely through the streets. They wore fur hats and Siberian mukluks, he said, and were taking notes on what they saw. If the Russians were there, no one paid much attention. Defense Minister Danson said that, considering the clumsy efforts recently made by the Soviet Union to penetrate the Canadian security services, this was not entirely implausible.

Sig Sigvaldason, for one, was refusing to take anything seriously. He still didn't think anything could be much worse than arsenic poisoning or the mercury deposits analyzed in the fish of Ciauque Lake north of Yellowknife. (The mercury level was four times the acceptable level.) Nor had his confidence grown in the ability of Canadian government officials to administer intelligently the rich resources of the north. Sigvaldason knew that Cosmos augured badly for the whole region, but he kept his sense of humor. In the *Yellowknifer* he wrote, with some annoyance, that "We get the fallout and the southerners get the radiation." He also made the considered observation that the media now outnumbered the armed forces personnel of the Northern Command in Yellowknife by two to one. And where else did you have a general who only commanded forty soldiers? Another issue of the *Yellowknifer* proclaimed that "the only fallout one could observe so far were the media types who filled every available hotel space." Sigvaldason, with his wild gray beard and bulging chest that threatened to burst the buttons of his shirt, had become the prickly conscience of Yellowknife. The Indians in the villages, the trappers and environmentalists could now rest easy. Sigvaldason was charging to their rescue. The big Icelander remained skeptical, aloof, indignant as he witnessed the turmoil Cosmos had produced.

One story in particular must have amused Sigvaldason. An important scientific member of NEST informed the amazed Canadians before his arrival that he wished to operate incognito. His plan was to arrive at Fort Reliance, 500 miles north of Edmonton, with a brown attache case, more familiarly known as the Los Alamos briefcase. The briefcase contained an efficient radiation detection system for use in built-up areas. The scientist would walk through Fort Reliance monitoring radiation without drawing attention to himself. This method had always worked successfully in the past and didn't excite the population unnecessarily.

No one had told the gentleman (who was unfamiliar with local conditions) that there were no streets in Fort Reliance. The shacks were built on muskeg. Besides, it was winter. If you avoided the snarling, snapping half-wild dogs, you could easily suffer a severe frostbite. When the scientist arrived in Fort Reliance, he quickly changed his mind.

Four days after the satellite was reported to have come down, the press discovered their first sensational story. They were actually going to be able to photograph a piece of Cosmos. Moreover, it was a story that had much human interest. Unlike Bristow's spectrometer discovery, which just preceded this event, the new story could be televised and the picture sent around the world. The hit registered on a gamma ray spectrometer confirmed that pieces of Cosmos existed. Now the public could actually see a piece for themselves.

At 3:00 PM on Saturday, January 28, two young men named Mike Mobley and John Mordhurst were mushing their six-dog team over the Thelon River. Mobley came from Arizona and Mordhurst from Illinois. They had gone to the north on a kind of adventuresome exploration trip whose ostensible purpose was to trace the route of a well-known explorer named John Hornby who had died in the Barrens in 1927. Hornby had missed the caribou migration that year and, along with a brave young Englishman, starved and froze to death.

Mordhurst and Mobley were now heading for the site where Hornby had died. Armed with radios and emergency equipment, they faced little danger of death by either starvation or cold. When they left their four comrades back in the base camp at Warden's Grove, about seventy miles south of Yellowknife in the uninhabited Thelon Game Sanctuary, they told them they would return shortly. The six men were doing some fish and wildlife studies as well as passing meteorological information along to certain Canadian government agencies. It was a commendable enterprise, one of hundreds of self-initiated outdoor adventures that take place in the Canadian north every year. And it might never have been reported except for the chance occurence which took place that Saturday afternoon. Their unplanned rendezvous with a twisted piece of metal was to give them all some brief fame.

As Mobley and Mordhurst came around the river bend they braked their dog team to a sudden halt. Inside a small, shallow, pock-marked crater, about eight feet across, were pieces of metal that looked as if they belonged in some junkyard. Several twisted metal tubes were disconnected from a squashed canister. The metal was charred and frosted over. It didn't look like part of an abandoned snowmobile. The two men wondered whether the low-flying Hercules aircraft they had seen throughout the day was in any way connected. The object had dug into the snow and burned an irregular pattern, forming a patch of smooth black ice. Mordhurst reached out and touched the metal briefly with a gloved hand. But he kept away from the wet black ice. Both men wondered what burned-out pieces of tubing were doing lying in the middle of this sub-arctic wilderness. Other smaller pieces of metal were strewn along a path leading to the crater. About five minutes later they shouted to their dogs to mush and continued to Hornby Point where the explorer whose route they wished to follow had perished almost exactly half a century before.

When they arrived back at their base camp in Warden's Grove, Mordhurst and Mobley told their four colleagues of the strange encounter in the wilderness. Some hours later, by a relayed radio connection through Fort Reliance, the group succeeded in making contact with Yellowknife and reported the event. The men at Warden's Grove had already heard about the satellite on the radio and thought the piece of metal could be connected with Cosmos. A short time later an excited message was transmitted to the explorers' camp that they should not approach closer than 1,000 feet to the object. They thought the whole matter was a bit of a joke, but next morning a Canadian military Twin Otter landed on skis at their camp. As they boarded the plane, Mordhurst and Mobley jokingly shouted, "Unclean, we're unclean," at the pilot. They had no idea what awaited them. The pilot was not in any mood to joke. The two adventurers were flown off to Yellowknife and then to Edmonton. After a series of tests they were found to be uncontaminated.

The world press and television crews had been eagerly searching for days for some visible evidence that Cosmos had actually come to the Barrens. So far they had been shown graphs, spoken to men with hand-held counters wearing yellow suits and face masks, been briefed by public relations officers and told of the dangers of radiation sickness. Everything about the operation looked and sounded very good. But no dramatic discoveries were being fed to the home public by the hundred or more media men and women who expected the appearance of some big event which would shock a public who were rapidly growing immune to shock. However, the fear of nuclear radiation was still a tremendously emotive subject.

Now a chance encounter made the big story. Mobley and Mordhurst were interviewed until they were dizzy, bewildered by all the fuss. Who were they? What were they doing in the wilderness of the Barrens? Had they been contaminated? Were they on a secret mission? Still wearing, as they would for several weeks, their breeches, thick ski socks, suspenders and lumberjack shirts, they seemed to enjoy the change from the hard bush life. They weighed offers from the press, stayed at a fine Edmonton hotel and were employed by Colonel Garland to help give first-hand information in the Warden's Grove area. But while the two adventurers were basking in the attention, more important events were taking place elsewhere.

Paul Mudra, a NEST geophysicist, left for the site on the Thelon River hours after Mordhurst and Mobley made their discovery. The metal parts which would eventually be removed by the AECB were not very radioactive and were not near the reactor. Mudra, one of the most capable men of the NEST team, would now make his own analysis.

When he heard the news of the discovery, Mudra had just returned from the most northeastern location of the footprint at Baker Lake. The early hits indicated that the search should be largely concentrated at the western end of the footprint, in the Yellowknife, Resolution and Snowdrift regions.

Paul Mudra has been chief of his division at Las Vegas for a large portion of his fifteen years with the Department of Energy. In Canada he was not asked to do organizational work as he presumed he would, but instead was sent out into the field, which he preferred.

Mudra had undertaken a number of missions in which he flew westward from Baker Lake in a Chinook helicopter. The western zones, after four days, became the concentrated center of the search as the gamma ray spectrometers registered an increasing number of small hits in this area. Near the tiny community of Snowdrift, Richard Lynn and Joe Tinney, with their microprocessing system, found man-made radiation sources in places previously declared uncontaminated. This was quite puzzling. Meanwhile, in the midst of all the excitement over the adventurers' chance discovery, Mudra flew by helicopter to examine the twisted metal struts inside the eight-foot crater. Analytical, knowledgeable and original, he was the ideal man to reconstruct the superficial history of the piece of shapeless metal lying in its sepulchre in the snow.

It was a bright sunlit day in the sub-zero temperature. The cold air gave an extra sharpness to the ice-coated features of the four-foot-long contraption lying in the crater. The metal, thought Mudra, was part of the satellite's propulsion unit. He felt sure of that. It certainly was not part of the core. Although he had been informed it was not radioactive, on contact Mudra's detector showed 15 Roentgens. This was a hazard, but the radiation would dissipate quickly in the air. A prolonged exposure at close range could, however, cause a health problem. Mudra's trained eye began to amass a wealth of important detail. Added to the information would be a degree of confusion that would confound Mudra and others for a while until a rational explanation was advanced. The twisted metal which Mudra described as "a plate, and cylinder with several appendages" was an odd structure. It could not constitute a danger to a passing hunter since the crater was marked out with orange tape and the object would soon be transported for chemical analysis to the Whiteshell nuclear laboratories at Pinawa.

What confused Mudra was the nature of the material. Since it did not seem to have been close to Cosmos' enriched uranium core, Mudra surmised that a shield of lithium had surrounded the object on the ground. When it struck the ice this heated lithium hissed and splattered on contact in a display of pyrotechnics that, according to Mudra, "must have been a spectacular sight to observe." But the phenomenon of brilliant light bursting like a series of giant-sized sparklers in the early morning had died unseen on the dark Barrens.

What really confounded Mudra more than anything else was the location of the object. He knew how the shallow crater was formed and could understand the pock-marks formed by the exploding lithium. He related all this to Scott MacDonald, who accompanied him to the site. MacDonald was a Canadian expert on snow and ice conditions and had been of great assistance to Mudra in differentiating between phenomena caused by nature and wildlife and that which was man-made. Perhaps there was more material that had burned itself into the ice which was now frozen over. All that could easily be determined. Mudra considered what had occurred at Fort Reliance, 140 miles to the west, two days before. Witnesses there had seen the satellite heading northeast. Not far from the town a small piece of highly radioactive material, only inches long, had been located in one of the early gross searches. At a distance of ten feet the fragment gave a reading of 200 Roentgens. This was lethal. It had been handled gingerly with long tongs and dropped into one of the lead containers supplied by the AECB. The high radioactivity of this metal indicated it had been close to the uranium core of Cosmos. Simple ballistics told Mudra that the core and its surrounding material, having greater weight than any other part of the satellite, should be carried much further to the east. Logically, this piece of debris should have been further down range than the large lithium-encased object. But it was not.

Scott MacDonald, who had a very wide knowledge of the north, was stationed at Baker Lake when Mudra arrived there. The geophysicist had posed MacDonald a number of questions about the nature of ice formation. If the core had landed intact or partially intact, could it, Mudra asked, have crashed through the ice of one of the thousands of lakes? Its great heat on re-entry might, be conjectured, have melted several feet of ice or snow and caused it to disappear from sight.

MacDonald told Mudra that this was possible but unlikely. At the present $-40°$, three-foot-thick ice would take about a week to freeze again to its original depth. MacDonald and Mudra drilled a number of ice core samples to test the theory, and MacDonald's information seemed correct. He also related how small herds of musk ox had the odd habit of tramping down crater-like depressions. These peculiar circular paddocks could look like man-made craters. Often as Mudra crossed the frozen lakes aboard the Chinook he would see at first hand the odd depressions in the snow.

But there still appeared to be something wrong with the calculations of reentry. The dispersal of Cosmos fragments on breakthrough had not been determined. No one had yet conceived the idea that there could have been a huge field of contamination of minute-sized particles. The prevalent theory was that the core, or parts of it, was somewhere on the footprint. Air samplings and gross searches proved radioactive dust did not exist. Neither the Canadian scientists, nor NEST, questioned the results of the equipment. Lynn and Tinney were perplexed by those dozens of low-level radiation readings around Snowdrift, but this was on the footprint and possibly not too unusual. Perhaps Lynn didn't pay too much close attention to the readings because the same day he became aware of them his helicopter made a forced landing near Fort Reliance. When he jumped onto the snow from the plane his feet broke through the hard crust and he stepped into a freak pool of water. In seconds his mukluks were soaked through. He had the presence of mind to rush back to the plane to take off his boots and narrowly avoided a severe frostbite.

Mudra was familiar with nuclear rocket ballistics, and as he looked at the fragment of Cosmos he thought of the American ramjet engine in which the nuclear reactor super-heated air and ejected it at high velocity. There could be a similarity between this nuclear engine and the Russian one. The cylinder and appendages bore a certain resemblance to some of the parts with which the geophysicist was familiar.

Mudra and MacDonald returned to the Chinook. The blades of the helicopter were still turning over. It was late and the pilot was anxious to get started on the two-and-a-half-hour return flight to Baker Lake.

As Mudra and MacDonald were returning to Baker Lake in the helicopter, Mudra looked down at the magnificent country. He was captivated by the rough beauty of the Barrens, and hoped this great natural storehouse would never be ravaged by man-made contamination. Then a horrible idea struck him. Suppose the core had disintegrated into a million pieces. High flying tests had proved that there was no radioactive cloud in the upper atmosphere. Maybe radioactive particles were slowly settling over the Barrens. The thought was terrifying.

Meanwhile, Robert Grasty of the Canadian Geological Survey was keeping a private record of the data he collected as he flew on his search missions across Great Slave Lake. Time and again he would try and visualize the results if someone took a giant pepper shaker and shook it high in the atmosphere above the ice. He tried to figure out what might occur if the shaker released radioactive particles instead of pepper. There was a peculiar wave action in the air above Great Slave Lake that preoccupied the paleogeologist. Also there was an unusual amount of radon – an element emitted during the decomposition of uranium. It was too early to disclose any findings because he didn't have sufficient data. So far what information he had gathered he didn't like. But sooner or later Grasty intended to find out the whole truth.

At command headquarters in hangar five a kind of controlled bedlam prevailed. Planning meetings were held by Colonel Garland daily at 10:00 AM. Present were several members of Garland's staff, Mahlon Gates (when he was there) and Troy Wade of DOE, senior US scientific advisor Richard Wagner, Roger Eaton of AECB, Keith Richardson from Geological Survey, John Doyle, equipment chief of EG&G and numerous scientists who had special information to contribute. Before the huge wall maps of the footprint in Garland's operation room, the day's operations would be determined and search results discussed. Listening in would be Dave Jackson and Lieutenant Colonel Beverley Totman of Canadian Forces public relations. The meetings were lively affairs: many ideas would be offered and rejected, but Garland would hold the reins.

By January 30, two large fragments and several dozen smaller pieces of Cosmos that had been found were forming a preliminary pattern whereby the scientists could predict what areas of the footprint were most likely to produce the most fruitful results.

11

Eighteen thousand square miles was a great deal of territory to cover looking for small metal fragments. With so many people from so many organizations embracing so many skills, there had to be confusion in spite of Colonel Garland's cohesive operational plan. The special Hit Evaluation Panel formed at the beginning of the operation and headed by Richard Wagner carefully weighed the daily results of the search and decided the best way to proceed. Someone had to decide which hits were accurate and which should be given priority with the facilities at hand. Everything had to be evaluated for its immediate or future damage to human life.

The NEST group was unusually cautious in its language. Barnett Danson, the Defense Minister, said on many occasions that there would be no information withheld by Canada, and at the time he probably meant what he said. But pretty soon the scientists of the AECB became tight-lipped and officious in their statements. But most of the other Canadians were still quite open. The conditions one met at the Department of Energy's controlled laboratories and institutions were a good deal stricter than they were in Canada. A foreigner couldn't enter an outer office or a laboratory connected with the production of atomic weapons. And a Canadian was classified as a foreigner. The world that members of NEST came from was different from the one in which they now functioned.

The Hercules, flying down the footprint, carried the sophisticated equipment to make the initial hit and mark it on the map. The location of the hit would be transmitted to one of the helicopter teams who would try to locate the site and land with hand-held detectors. These would in turn identify the precise position of the debris, which could be visible or buried in the snow. The method was a good one except that no one really knew if the hits could be found the second time around in the helicopter, even though the approximate map coordinates were given. The official explanation for the difficulty was that because the object was embedded in the snow it sent up a thin pencil of radiation that could very easily be missed by the ground team unless there was a more precise way of plotting the source.

Then again, no one knew how large the finds would be. A large amount of radiation could come from a relatively small piece of metal, while a large piece of the satellite might produce a low reading on the spectrometer. Therefore, navigating accurately to within a hundred feet or less of the source became as important as detecting the radiation. In a country that did not have accurate maps and where one lake and hill looked pretty much like another, this wasn't always easy. To solve the navigation problem, NEST brought up their microwave-ranging system after the first week of the search. There was only one available in North America at the time and it was installed in a Hercules aircraft. This allowed the plane to fly a close grid search and pinpoint their position at any given time to within a few feet. Now the Hercules aircraft could fly the area with exceptional accuracy and transmit the exact coordinates of any radioactive material to the helicopters.

To further clarify the reentry trajectory a number of scientists from Livermore, the Aerospace Corporation and the Sandia laboratories at Los Alamos arrived in Edmonton at the end of January. After all, they had now found two large pieces and half a dozen small fragments of Cosmos, so a more accurate picture of the satellite's path could be constructed. The aerospace engineers produced more theories which, when summarized, said that the original path worked out by Morrison and Bell had been correct. But Colonel Garland probably made the most telling remark when he said, referring to the two explorers, "It took the human eyeball to make the first important discovery. From a technical point of view, what Mobley and

Mordhurst discovered was a vital part of Cosmos."

With the new microwave-ranging system much of the guess-work in locating debris was removed. This took a great weight off Garland's mind. With each day he became increasingly aware that he was racing against time to find the remains of Cosmos. If the assessment of the scientists on the Hit Evaluation Panel was correct, there would be large numbers of small fragments to recover. The months ahead, preceding the spring breakup, were the most grueling: temperatures would be low, men and machines would be severely taxed. No one knew how much time they had left before spring, and no one knew what they would actually find. Recovery of debris, though made easier by the microwave ranging system, would still be difficult: sometimes it took six or seven flights over a single small area. But at least now, when a hit was recorded, it was not only printed on a magnetic tape but the precise longitude and latitude of the site were simultaneously fixed. There was a permanent record of every hit.

Other haphazard techniques were also regularized. After they had identified the location of the fragment a helicopter team flew directly to the site and dropped an identification marker (usually a streamer or a flare). Another helicopter carrying AECB personnel would then land at the site, shovel the snow and debris into a black plastic garbage bag, and put it into a specially lined steel drum. The drum would be flown away to Namao and kept in one of the base's underground ammunition bunkers. The next day it would be shipped for analysis to the Whiteshell Atomic Energy laboratories at Pinawa, Manitoba.

At first the radioactive pieces were transported by commercial Air Canada flights. When Defense Minister Danson heard this, he exploded. The repercussions could have been considerable if passengers had known they were sitting above hazardous pieces of radioactive metal. Fortunately, they never found out. And Danson immediately ordered that all future shipments go by military planes.

Conflicting opinions, ideas and explanations prevailed in

those early days. Ross Brown of the AECB said that the criterion for removal of debris was whether it gave a reading higher than 500 micro-roentgens (a micro-roentgen is one millionth of a roentgen). Garland, on the other hand, said that no such criterion had been established.

At the same time, personalities began to assert themselves among the scientists. Wagner might have found Grasty often distinctly irritating, and Grasty could not penetrate the wall of Wagner's impassivity. He also questioned the entire concept of the search pattern and sometimes had fundamental doubts about Wagner himself. But lack of sleep and the constant tension affected perspective. The Americans, unlike the Canadians, were unified as a team and behaved with conformity. Grasty had his own views on all subjects relating to Operation Morning Light – for instance, the importance of wind in determining the pattern of contamination. Dave Jackson was beginning to feel uncomfortable in the dominant role he had assumed in directing most of the Canadian public relations activity. Grasty struggled to suppress his feelings among the unemotional NEST men. NEST came to Canada to help but only Canada would suffer the contamination.

After a week, the long, punishing hours aggravated personality differences. The NEST personnel had been told that they would be away for forty-eight hours. By the end of the first eight days it was apparent that this was only the beginning of Morning Light. Days passed very quickly and for most of the searchers they were only measured by what they found. A hit became the supreme moment. Workers would be rotated after the first three weeks, replaced by their counterparts. The days passed in a gray blur of time, one day hardly distinguishable from the one before or the one after. The men and women involved in the search did not mind the long hours. It was a kind of war game where the big prize was the discovery of Cosmos' reactor core. The hunt generated its own excitement. No one really wanted to miss the event.

Supply and fuel problems had to be solved. The long haul from Namao to the search area was costly and time-consuming.

The strain on men and machine was an unnecessary handicap to the search. Twin Otters and helicopters based in Yellowknife were often flying at the end of their fuel range. Because of these difficulties, important search time was wasted. It was soon decided that an intermediary supply camp had to be built.

The camp had already been given the name of Camp Garland after the operational commander and would consist of thermally insulated and heated tents for the planes and suitable living quarters for the personnel. It would be built on a lake to be christened Cosmos Lake, and it had to be made operational in winter, while the four-foot-thick ice could still carry the 78,000-pound dead weight of the Hercules. Fuel supplies, food and scientific instruments would be flown in immediately. But first a runway must be cleared on the ice. A bulldozer had to be dropped on the lake by the ingenious LAPES technique (Low Altitude Parachute Extraction System). In this operation, a Hercules aircraft flew about four feet above level ground with its rear loading hatch wide open. Two parachutes were attached to a bulldozer solidly strapped to a wooden platform. The first smaller parachute pulled out a second larger one, which in turn violently yanked the bulldozer from the plane. The pilot had to have a good eye. Frequently he skimmed just above the terrain. There was no margin for error.

This bulldozer would be dropped without delay. The ice on the lakes would break up in late May and by early April the ice would already become too soft for the heavy-weight Hercules to land. Special tents to be used as hangars, fuel dumps and living quarters were gathered overnight and stored at Namao ready to be flown in to Lake Cosmos the moment the bulldozer crew had completed its job.

12

In the intervening time two strange reports made their appearance in military circles in Ottawa and introduced a rather bizarre element into Operation Morning Light. One was ignored but could have considerable relevance. It came from a trained observer and experienced navigator. The other was in the realm of psychic phenomena and for some reason had the label "restricted" attached. If psychic phenomena had meaning, this one sounded somewhat ominous.

Costa Kruger is a Swede who served thirty years as navigator in the Scandinavian Airlines Systems. During his long career he has flown the polar route from Scandinavia to North America more times than he could remember. On January 26, Kruger flew (as a passenger, for a change) on a SAS flight SK933, leaving Stockholm at 11:25 AM Greenwich Mean Time. The navigator was traveling to San Francisco, where he would be met by his daughter and son-in-law and taken to their new home in nearby San Jose. The flight was to make a single stop at Seattle, where passengers flying on to San Francisco would not be able to disembark. Kruger noticed that the flight plan took the aircraft along the familiar track "Charlie" to the northeastern coast of Canada, following from there the VHF omnirange beacons that were stationed at intervals over the Northwest Territories. Kruger was quite familiar with the route and the terrain. He could plot the tracking stations from memory as if he had been navigating the Boeing 707 himself. As the plane approached the Mackenzie River district the pilot announced to the passengers that they were in the vicinity of the region where the Russian satellite Cosmos 954 was reported to have landed. The altitude then was about 35,000 feet.

Kruger looked at his watch, which he kept on GMT. It was a little after 19.00 hours, which would make it 2:00 PM local time. The weather was remarkably clear, cloudless, almost dazzling. The sun shone down on the thousands of snow-covered lakes and over the stunted pine trees, outlining every feature in brilliant detail. The plane's shadow could be seen moving over the pure white landscape, and the shapes of the frozen lakes were easily identifiable. They were smooth on the surface, snow-blown, surrounded by small hills. But the whiteness was unbroken, endless, a world buried in snow and blasted by freezing, ferocious winds. On the ground, Kruger mused, every small exertion would require monumental effort. From his warm and comfortable seat by the window, well fed and attended, the navigator stared below. He had an unobstructed vista of the terrain for great distances. Less than a hundred miles to the northwest were the small Indian communities of Reliance, Snowdrift and Rat Lodge. Even odd isolated cabins could be seen like brown cubes set in the white wilds of the Barrens. Seldom had Kruger enjoyed such a perfect view.

Then suddenly, directly below on one of the large lakes, Kruger saw something peculiar. He looked again but the object had not changed. There was no doubt in his mind. It was some kind of unnatural opening in the ice. From a distance it looked quite small, but it must have been about 500 to 1000 feet in diameter. The hole was almost circular. Kruger became very excited. Remembering that the pilot had announced they were flying over the reported landing place of the Russian satellite, he looked closely again. Over the hole was a large vapor trail which drifted west-southwest. The wind must be blowing it. Kruger had read the report of the crash of the satellite in the Swedish press. The newspaper had said that the space vehicle had been powered by a uranium core which could cause great heat, maybe some kind of explosion when it struck the earth. This deserted lake could be the place of impact. Kruger kept his face pressed against the window until the plane passed over the area. In the former navigator's mind there was no mistake. He had never been more definite about anything in his life. When he lost sight of the lake, Kruger, still exhilarated by the discovery, jumped up and hurried toward the cockpit. He was known to the crew. He wanted the latitude and longitude of the position the plane had passed over a few minutes ago. It would not be difficult to back-track their location.

What surprised Kruger most of all was that no one else on the flight, including the crew, had seen the hole in the ice or the vapor trail drifting above the lake. But he was positive that he had seen it, and was most anxious to tell the people who were searching for the satellite. Some military authority somewhere should be made aware of the news, but he didn't know how that could be done. He would not be allowed off the plane when it touched down in a few hours at Seattle.

Then he had an idea. He would write a letter, give it to one of the ground crew at Seattle, and ask that it be delivered to the nearest military post. Kruger had no idea if his message would be received or given any attention by the authorities. But he was mistaken. The SAS ground official at Seattle who took the letter contacted the local police. They were told the message came from one of SAS's navigators, and it was treated seriously.

Captain R.G. Nelson of the Police Department of the Port of Seattle took one look at Kruger's letter and sent it immediately to the Security Police at the McCord Air Force base. The whole world knew about Cosmos 954.

On the same day, January 26, the Washington headquarters of the United States Air Force telexed the contents of Kruger's message to the Department of Energy. From there it went instantly through the DOE communications system to Namao. The telex that came to Garland's desk at operations headquarters read:

The following message received 13.39 hours this date in a sealed envelope by the department – "from SAS SK933 undersigned Costa Kruger. Observed big, absolutely round hole (approximate diameter 300–500 feet) in the snow-covered ice of a lake with position 60 degrees 48 minutes north, 106 degrees 15 minutes west at 19.10 G.M.T., January 26th, 1978.

West of the hole there was a vapor trail about five times the size of the hole dribbling w.s.w. The weather was absolutely clear over that area. I am flying as a passenger but having 30 years as navigator in SAS, I got the position from INS (Inertia Navigational System). Can that position be the impact of the Russian satellite? On board SAS SK933 CPG-SEA January 26th, 1978. C. Kruger, Braxenvaegen II, S-18131, Lidinove, Sweden."

No one thoroughly investigated Kruger's report. No one really had the time or the inclination since it was south of the footprint. It was the early days of the search and the men cruising up the thirty-mile-wide corridor between Yellowknife and Baker Lake were having great difficulty investigating closely all the hits reported from the gamma ray spectrometers. The aircraft were all working day and night and so were the men. There were no machines nor personnel to spare to immediately check new reports. The two baby helicopters carried to Namao in the bodies of the C141 jets were still unassembled in the warmth of hangar five; they would be like dinky toys, a danger to men and instruments, if they were exposed to the inhuman cold of the frozen Barrens. They could not be used. Therefore, during the short daylight hours and the long nights the men dedicated themselves to the predetermined search area with their existing equipment. The searchers were not inclined to be distracted. If Kruger had actually seen a large hole in the ice, within forty-eight hours a film of ice would have already formed over the water. Within another forty-eight hours the ice could be a foot or more thick. By then the vapor cloud would have dispersed and there would be no trace.

At the beginning of February an increasing number of small particles were preoccupying the attention of the search teams. Some were so small they couldn't be seen and were shoveled with the snow into the black plastic garbage bags and then sealed in drums to be sent to Whiteshell. This buckshot-like material was appearing with great regularity in a southern direction from Reliance toward the position reported by Kruger. Much of the radioactive material was found in the two new zones, nine and ten, that had recently been drawn on the huge map in Garland's operation room.

Roger Eaton of the AECB admitted they had made a mistake. No one had fully taken into account the effect of the wind. But he only reflected a viewpoint that was becoming obvious.

The small particles blown by the wind were sufficiently radioactive to be dangerous to man or beast. How prevalent the tiny particles were no one knew. Grasty was one of the scientists becoming increasingly preoccupied with the phenomenon. No doubt, the scientists concluded, these particles were bits of the core. If Kruger's hole in the ice was really made by a heavy piece of enriched uranium then the increasing number of radioactive particles reported represented only a tiny fraction of the core. If a large piece of uranium fell into a lake then the water might shield humans from the dangerous effect for a while. However, the clear cold lakes spill into one another in the spring breakup. Streams are a circuit of flowing veins that feed each other. Life does not stand still. Fish move from lake to river to stream to eventual human consumption. In this great storehouse of natural wealth the tiniest organism is on the move, in agitation. After the long winter sleep the land bursts into feverish activity. It would be a mistake to think that a huge chunk of enriched uranium 235 would be safe in a lake in the Northwest Territories. If the hole Kruger saw that afternoon staring out of the window of the plane was made by a solid part of the reactor core of Cosmos then the Barrens one day may yield up the secret.

There had been much speculation about the equipment Cosmos carried. In the long search for pieces of debris no one from NEST or the AECB talked about the purpose of the satellite's mission. That seemed to have no importance to the searchers: their single-minded purpose left no time for any idle speculation. The Americans went out of their way to stress that their only interest was the cleanup of the debris. Nothing else counted. Whenever one asked if the satellite was orbiting the earth on a special mission, the answer was a variation of the theme, "Well, all I know is what I read in the papers." General Gates pleaded innocence and Defense Minister Danson said he had "no idea what the satellite was supposed to be doing." The bland, naive replies were disarming. After all, the United States Department of Energy came under the Defense Department, which had to take some interest in what Cosmos was doing orbiting over the North American continent and adjacent waters.

The NEST photographer, Kirk Knighton, was out daily in the field taking hundreds of pictures with his special photographic equipment. Most of them were intended not for the public but for scientific and possibly military study. All were extremely detailed, recording the debris from every conceivable angle. These photos would be classified and unavailable even upon special request. The ordinary people of the world were very interested in Cosmos. They were both interested and fearful of its radiation and its mission in space. The authorities had kept their silence about the existence of the danger. Perhaps now they might be more forthcoming about the purpose of the satellite. The first silence might have been justified on the grounds that it would avoid panic among the population. However, this second silence was justified in the name of national security.

A weird, unworldly element was introduced into the speculation that already surrounded the space object. It was an odd theory but no more outlandish than the entire fantastic experience of the reentry and the sudden appearance of instruments and men that hardly anyone had heard of before.

On January 26, the same day that Costa Kruger made his sighting, F.R. Cleminson of the Foreign Liaison branch of the Canadian Department of Defense had a strange visitor to his office in Colonel By Drive, Ottawa. The visitor's name was Earl G. Curley and he was accompanied by an official from the Department of Defense.

Curley was a quite ordinary-looking man. He was thirty-one years old, of medium height, had black hair and wore a dark, conservative suit. The only elements in his appearance that could be thought of as unusual were his black, darting eyes that seemed to sum people up quickly. What was truly remarkable about Curley, however, was his occupation. He was a psychic.

Earl Curley had recognized strange powers in himself at the age of three, when a vision of his dead father appeared to him. Now he made no fuss about his psychic abilities. It was all quite matter-of-fact. For several years he had been employed by a number of industrial firms and individuals to make forecasts about their business activities. And he had uncanny success.

On January 10, 1977, Curley predicted in the occult *Inner Life Magazine* that a Soviet satellite would come down in the north. This was a year before it happened. On January 23, 1978, a day before Cosmos broke into the atmosphere, Curley told Captain Joseph Dick, a US Naval attaché in Ottawa, that the satellite would be coming down the next day. This extraordinary insight he treated naturally and preferred that no one consider him extraordinary.

In calm, reasoned tones, the clairvoyant described to Cleminson his vision. He had seen the entire reentry of Cosmos over the Yellowknife district. The satellite had broken into three main pieces, he said, and a number of smaller ones. For the location of the reactor core, which he stated was wholly or partially intact, he gave a set of coordinates.

Cleminson listened to Curley for about an hour. He wasn't sure whether the man was guessing or had genuine visionary powers, and decided to treat the meeting and its contents as "restricted." Cleminson told the psychic that although he himself had no responsibility for the search he would see that any report he compiled would be delivered to the correct people. Curley understood this and said he would return next morning with a full written report. Everything he wanted to say was already in his mind. It would take him several hours to write it all down.

Next morning at 7:40 the psychic arrived at Cleminson's office with a ten-page report. It didn't mean very much to the officer in the Foreign Liaison because he couldn't verify the details. No one had the details at that early date. The search was only beginning. Curley had looked at the map of the Northwest Territories and after a few minutes took some notes and said that the search should be concentrated at

(a) 63° 17′ N. 109° 50° W.
(b) 63° 38′ N. 108° 15° W.

The latitudes were slightly off but the longitude would eventually be proven accurate. These districts around Snowdrift and Fort Reliance would have the greatest concentrations of particles.

The people at operations in Namao might have glanced at the report briefly with some amusement and then cast it aside. At Namao they were all pragmatists. Perhaps they weren't aware that for twenty-five years the Russians have been experimenting in considerable depth in psychic research and were said to be using psychics in a number of scientific endeavors.

Curley insisted that the satellite's purpose was to manipulate the weather system of the world by altering the energy belt surrounding the earth's atmosphere. For a number of years NASA and other agencies in the US had been experimenting with satellites that could alter weather patterns. It was not inconceivable that the Russians were doing the same.

Curley's report was filed away and affixed with the label "classified," and no one heard of it again. Between a psychic and a navigator to whom no one paid much attention, new and interesting avenues of speculation had been opened and then closed just as suddenly. To advance theories that were out of the ordinary and then investigate them thoroughly required supporters who could command the resources and marshal the time. The people who could have undertaken the investigation were too deeply committed elsewhere in Morning Light to bother.

13

The hunt continued into February with unabated energy, but the results were disappointing. If new facts were emerging the men who had them were not talking. There was a good deal of movement between Las Vegas, Livermore, Ottawa, Edmonton and Yellowknife. Scientists and DOE employees were continually flying back and forth in a kind of shuttle service. The search activity, far from being spectacular, was a slow and tedious process. After the first sensational finds the discoveries were all of small pieces, sprayed like pepper from Robert Grasty's hypothetical pepper shaker.

The space age that had brought with it the romance of conquest of distant planets and the exploration of outer galaxies seemed to be ending on the Barrens in nightmarish fashion. The golden age of space adventure that reached beyond our imagination became an extension of our aggression on earth. Its competitiveness was bringing civilization close to the brink. Cosmos had no warhead but in the minds of everyone the unknown fear was there. The satellite was some kind of omen to those far removed from the area.

Behind the anxiety lay the unconscious fear of nuclear radiation that goes back to the memory of Hiroshima and Nagasaki. That memory is now thirty-three years old. But the fear that began there has increased rather than diminished. Therefore it was not unnatural that people everywhere, especially the young, were concerned about a satellite whose mission they didn't fully understand and an area of contamination that nobody could define.

The seeds of misunderstanding grew when the AECB refused to release any information about their laboratory findings at

Whiteshell. W.K.Gummer, manager of the Planning and Coordination Division of the AECB, said: "no photographs or information about the analysis of the research done at the Atomic Energy of Canada Whiteshell laboratories would be available." This was a disturbing statement to be made by a public official to a member of the public. The searchers were supposedly engaged on a peacetime mission. Surely the secrets were not so profoundly disturbing that they could not be revealed.

One of the great mysteries of the search, never fully explained, occurred as early as January 26. The gamma ray spectrometer on a Hercules, flying at 1,000 feet, registered two highly radioactive sources. The plane was 200 miles east-northeast of Fort Reliance – a place that never again produced a spectrometer reading. A team of scientists, among whom were two US health physicists and Paul Mudra, went to Baker Lake at the eastern extremity of the footprint to further investigate. The hit was powerful enough to suggest that the core, or at least part of it, had been discovered. But the source was never relocated. Officials explained the violent reaction on the detection equipment as having been caused by a malfunction. But the same equipment had continued in use and worked perfectly. There were more mysteries to clear up than the reports of Costa Kruger and Earl Curley. Maybe the human eye would be the decisive factor in the search. As Lieutenant Colonel Bill Butchart of Northern Command at Yellowknife would comment later, "Operation Morning Light was like looking for a few hundred needles in a haystack 18,000 miles square." He didn't know at the time he was conservative in his comparison. The size of that haystack would be enlarged greatly, but the area of intensive search much reduced.

However, the difficulty of finding a source of radiation the second time around was known to every uranium prospector waiting quietly on the side lines to stake his claims in the new territory Morning Light had opened up. Prospectors said the cone of radiation from uranium deposits was narrow at the top and wide at the base, and therefore the planes were flying too high. The helicopters flying at twenty-five feet, slithering like crabs sideways up and down over the contours of the land were at the right level to pick up the pieces of Cosmos. But prospecting for Cosmos was a good deal different from searching for large deposits of natural uranium.

By the middle of February the AECB had packaged in their expensive containers many scraps of metal that looked like shrapnel fragments picked up by World War II souvenir hunters on the Normandy beaches. However, anyone handling any of the hot radioactive pieces without proper precautions would soon have a nasty burn. The effects of that burn could be lethal. The radiation poison could act in a few days, a week or in years. Although the average man might view the AECB display as radioactive junk, to the scientists and military personnel its value exceeded that of any rare metal. The secrets it yielded could be priceless.

A number of techniques evolved in the method of safeguarding and retrieving the debris in remote areas. No matter where in the wilderness parts of Cosmos landed, there was always a chance that someone could stumble across them. Usually a constable of the RCMP or a small detachment of Canadian Forces personnel was sent in by plane or parachute to guard the site. They would set up camp (a single tent) on the frozen tundra or near a lake. Their purpose was to keep the Indians away from contaminated metal. If the hit looked particularly important the scientists would arrive as close to the site as they could by plane or helicopter and tramp to the debris on snowshoes. A yellow bunting usually circled off the area if the wind had not blown it away and the snow had not buried it.

For those who guarded the site, the best means of survival in the inhumanly cold weather was to sleep naked in thick down bags and remain within the tent. The temperature frequently dropped so low that skin froze the moment it was exposed.

Each piece was clandestinely flown to the Whiteshell laboratory, transferred into special lead flasks and then slid into the hot cells for a comprehensive examination of its physical properties. In the concrete-walled rooms of the hot cells the material was examined by skilled technicians through lead glass windows and handled with remote manipulator arms. The metals underwent every conceivable analytical test, minutely scrutinized with the complex Van de Graff accelerator. The scientists at Whiteshell were extracting from every shipment the most complete information about Cosmos. When the autopsy of the remains was complete the results were labeled top-secret.

In early February the Hit Evaluation Panel had stated that spectral analysis made near Yellowknife in zone one established the existence of an unknown number of fragments lying on or below the surface of the snow. The panel merely confirmed what would, by the middle of the month, begin to look suspiciously like some kind of pattern. But no one was sure whether it would continue. Fission products from the reactor itself had now been uncovered in random pockets. The size and intensity of the sources were in doubt for a few days, until the helicopters went in to measure the radioactivity and searchers shoveled the debris into containers.

The sources proved to be tiny pieces of metal, sufficiently radioactive to be dangerous upon prolonged exposure. If there were more pieces of the reactor core in the same area this would mean that the uranium power pack had disintegrated before any other part of the machine and had dispersed in the first few search zones. But there was insufficient evidence for the scientists to make a definitive judgment. They wanted absolute proof before they issued statements, especially with public attention focused on them.

Meanwhile, the search continued up and down the footprint, with slightly more emphasis being given to the zones in the vicinity of Great Slave Lake. Everyone knew that man-made radioactive fragments on the lake should be unmistakable since there was no background of natural uranium. Work continued with undiminished vigor. The searchers toiled on together through necessity. Troy Wade went far out of his way to cooperate and avoid any areas of contention between the Canadians and Americans. There was really too much for everyone to do to be concerned with rivalry. At the end of an eighteen-hour day either at operations headquarters or in the field, men were too tired to foster animosities.

Before Camp Garland was built the ground search teams operated out of Northern Command at Yellowknife. They were the NEST group and the AECB men, who did the most grueling physical work and flew in the helicopters. They landed in the wilderness and snowshoed in waist-deep snow to the site. They returned in the evening to the Explorer Hotel where they slept and ate their dinner. Through the thermopane windows of their rooms they could see where the Barrens began at the edge of town. In the chilling winter air of Yellowknife the chimney smoke billowed in crystalline clouds and hung for a long time over the houses.

With everyone involved in the search being too preoccupied or too tired to be interviewed, the press had to rely on the American and Canadian public relations men. The official reports issued by the Canadians were dull, often very brief documents written in stilted official language. They concentrated on defining the area of search:

Hercules over area 1
Hercules over area 4
Hercules over area 9
One Corvair over area 1 and 4 and track crawl area 1 through 5 inclusive.

The Canadians told a minimum about the search but if one compiled their statements over a long enough period it was possible to put together some kind of fragmented story.

Dave Jackson, on the other hand, was more practiced in journalism than the Canadians. He pushed his team of United States personnel into the public gaze as much as he could with a modicum of discretion. After all, that was what he was paid for. On the whole he was friendly and helpful. His press releases were generally more to the point than those of the Canadians:

> Canadian and Americans have established a camp on the ice at the extreme northeastern end of Great Slave Lake near Fort Reliance to take radiological measurements of an area where parts of the Russian satellite apparently have landed. The suspected area has been cordoned off with barrels and is under guard by Canadian Forces and the RCMP. The joint team are living in tents. EG&G, Inc., have been providing radiological support for the search and provided photos taken of the satellite object located near Warden's Grove.

This report was signed by Jackson. The ubiquitous Jackson didn't miss very much. When the excitement died after two weeks he returned to Las Vegas and sent an assistant as replacement.

Roger Eaton, scientific advisor to the AECB, served as scientific spokesman for the search operation, and he enjoyed his role. In most of his announcements he was conscious that his remarks might be published, and he usually tried to hedge his bets. The following example gives an idea of the style of his releases.

> We have picked up a piece of metal from our original hit site. This metal is 3″ long by 1″ in diameter and is silvery and shiny in color. It is 10–20 Roentgens per hour on contact. This is, I think, clearly the piece that we said was about 13 centimeters under the snow. We have also by chance picked up a very light piece of tubing, about one foot in diameter, approximately 2 feet long and approximate wall thickness $\frac{1}{4}$ inch which appears to have been exposed to extreme heat. I stress extremely light. It is not radioactive. The best estimate is that it is part of the satellite at the present moment and there is a chance, just a very long chance at this point, based on its apparent density, that it might be beryllium. We have no confirmation of that and we hope to have more information on this later.

Eaton didn't want to be wrong. The whole world was listening. Later he said he was wrong: the tubing was not beryllium. When asked what it was he did not reveal the type of metal.

This was a significant point. Beryllium is light in weight and characteristically used in reactors for reflectors and control mechanisms surrounding the core. It is also tremendously resistant to radioactivity. Fragments of the reactor had admittedly been located and now one had the material that surrounded the enriched uranium of the reactor. Together these two items indicated that the core, in one form or another, was now somewhere on the tundra or in the water that covered most of the Northwest Territories. Everything seemed to fit. When the scientific advisor said that his "best estimate is that it is part of the satellite at the present moment," he demonstrated a most extraordinary reticence, which increased with time. It was most unlikely that it could be anything other than the satellite, sitting as it was in the middle of Great Slave Lake in the winter wilderness. There is no plumbing 200 miles out of Yellowknife. But it was a chance discovery like most of the big important pieces, sighted by the human eye, and it demonstrated once more, the distribution pattern. The small pieces were falling short around the eastern portion of the Great Slave Lake and the heavier fragments further down-range.

All the available aircraft that the Canadian Forces could spare were put to work in Operation Morning Light. The use of any more in the corridor would be dangerous: all civilian planes were forbidden to fly over the search area. But it wan't necessarily the aircraft that were in short supply. It was more the nature of the objective that caused the difficulty. High-magnification aerial photographs taken almost daily for a week yielded only four negligible results. Two chance encounters in five days were responsible for the discovery of two large pieces of the satellite. The smaller, highly radioactive fragments were, it is true, detected by monitoring equipment. But this, too, was often chance. Following initial detection, a second run over the same place frequently failed to register, because of the different ways the radiation could be emitted. Also, the wind could affect where the particles fell. A slight wind-shift in the atmosphere could add hundreds of miles to the width of the footprint, which would then become only a rough guide to the whereabouts of the radioactive debris. But there could easily be other corridors. New dimensions could be added. Every time a chance discovery was made, new theories were born.

And perhaps more important than any other factor loomed the inexperience of the most experienced team of scientists in the world in the conditions under which they were working. It was one thing to do the experiments under rigorously controlled conditions in the Nevada Test Site but quite another when nature was in command. As General Gates said, Edmonton had the total US capability at its disposal for one rogue satellite. But the resources of the entire United States were inadequate to deal with the emergency on the Canadian Barrens. Moreover, there was still great perplexity, much unexpressed anxiety in high quarters of both the US and Canadian governments about the inadequacy of the forces employed in Morning Light.

On February 8 a special container was needed in a hurry to pick up a dangerous object laying on the ice in the Great Slave Lake near McLeod Bay. It was a small fragment, $10'' \times 3''$ thick – silvery in color, and flat and harmless-looking. It was examined and photographed at a distance and cordoned off with an RCMP and Canadian Forces detachment. Not far away, fifteen miles north east of Fort Reliance, two other "hot" fragments were also being located by ground parties, but this first fragment was the most dangerous. Instructions were given by the scientists to treat the rather dull bar of unknown metal with great respect. But no one required a warning. It had a maximum reading of 500 roentgens per hour: close contact for more than a few minutes could cause radiation sickness.

The University of Alberta Cancer Institute was asked to build in one night a lead container to house the highly radioactive metal. The lead box measured only $11'' \times 4'' \times 2''$, but it weighed 1,600 pounds. It was surrounded by layers of lead bricks, each 2 inches thick. The radioactive object was picked up by AECB technicians with long pincers in the presence of the

Canadian NAST squad, and gingerly lifted into the lead container. It was flown to Namao and stored in the bunkers near the airfield. That same day a Hercules departed with the metal for Whiteshell. At Whiteshell the results of the chemical analysis were as tightly sealed as the container in which the material was held. A wall of security surrounded the thorough research done at the nuclear establishment. Who and what was being protected was unclear and unstated. The AECB spokesmen, usually so happy to make newsworthy statements to the press and television, kept the important information to themselves.

14

Among the 270 inhabitants of the Indian village of Snowdrift, 100 miles east of Yellowknife, the arrival of Cosmos created an atmosphere of terror. At the beginning of February, out on the ice of Great Slave Lake, less than a mile from the village, a constable from the RCMP set up his arctic tent and began patrolling in his snowmobile in an effort to keep the Chipewyans out of certain areas. The next day four soldiers arrived by helicopter and helped the constable mark off these areas with brightly colored bunting. Then, as the curious Indians looked on, the soldiers fired off orange flares to attract the attention of the big four-engined planes that were flying in the vicinity. When the Indians went out to inspect the strange markings, the RCMP constables sternly ordered them to stay away.

This deeply worried the Chipewyans. Inbred for generations, they are easy prey to rumor and superstition. Later, when people arrived wearing yellow suits and carrying boxes which they ran up and down over the hair and bodies of all the villagers, the sense of panic was heightened. It was at this point that Brigadier General Kenneth Thornycroft decided to pay a visit to the village.

General Thornycroft is a most urbane, articulate and civilized man. He holds the rank of Commander of the Northern Region. When the search for Cosmos was at its height and the single-story wooden building of the Northern Command headquarters in Yellowknife bustling with scientists and helicopter pilots, Thornycroft was there too. He was tucked away out of sight in a back office. Few people, civilian or military, paid much attention to the general. As Lieutenant Colonel Bill Butchart frantically attempted to control the complex mechanism of the field search for Cosmos, Thornycroft in another part of the building was isolated from the action. The jurisdiction was quite clear. He attended to his affairs while the men under Colonel Garland at Namao were charged with finding what was left of Cosmos.

But Thornycroft is not a person to be easily forgotten, even though there are some people who say he was put in Yellowknife so he would be out of the way. And one surmises that you couldn't be much further out of the way than a back office in the Northern Command building at Yellowknife. The general has a responsibility for overseeing a land mass embracing 1.5 million square miles and has forty men to administer it. This would appear to many as a most bizarre circumstance, a role of comic opera proportions. Only two years before, Thornycroft led the Tenth Tactical Air Command out of Montreal. He is a former pilot himself; as he says, it was a "gung ho outfit." And when he talks about it his eyes sparkle and he remembers the days nostalgically. One's first tendency is to regard this soldier as a general who could not be retired officially but had been unofficially.

Thornycroft is a tall, lean man, vigorous and youthful in his carriage, somewhat retiring in his manner, dignified, assured. In the midst of the excitement, the coming and going of the scientists and pilots, the constant blare of radio communications, Thornycroft remained in isolation. The action swirled around but left him almost untouched. He was the liaison between the military and civilians in this mammoth territory, whose size is incomprehensible to him. But the general is slowly coming to terms with his alien existence, to the thousands of square miles of tundra and the few civilians who inhabit it. How can he conceive of a million lakes, rivers and streams, of villages of Indians whose thinking hasn't changed much since their forefathers led the entrepid Sir John Franklin up the Yellowknife 158 years ago? He takes his work seriously, although it may not have been what he wanted.

Thornycroft had the job of explaining the emergency to people who, by February 3, had become so frightened they thought they were all going to be sterilized by the pieces of satellite lying near their homes. The Chipewyans would listen to the general with much respect, but also with much suspicion.

In the community recreation hall in Snowdrift, most of the settlement gathered to listen to Thornycroft's explanations. There were certain difficulties. The interpreter, band councilor Felix Lockhart, himself a member of the tribe, couldn't find the exact translation for the word "radioactivity." There was none in the Chipewyan language, so he used the closest word, which came out as "poisonous." The interpreter said that the poison which had come out of the sky would not fall upon the villages, which puzzled the Indians. Less than a mile away on the lake, the RCMP constable prevented curious members of the tribe from approaching the place cordoned off with orange bunting.

Florence Catholique, known as the settlement chaperone, could not be appeased. She wanted confirmation that they would not all become sick, sterile and maybe die. There were too few Chipewyans in the world now. Their ancient enemy the Dog Ribs numbered as many. And there were old members of the community who still remembered the days when they used to raid mercilessly the enemy's camp. They wanted to live. The children wanted to live. The dogs, the caribou and the foxes also had a right to live.

Thornycroft, who had only been in Yellowknife a short while, had been cast more in the role of a mediator and diplomat than that of a soldier. Although one hill and lake looked the same as another to the general, to the Indian trappers each piece of their land had a special meaning. Through some of it the caribou passed; in other parts the migrating herds stopped in springtime for the cows to calf. No piece of the country was a dead place. Furthermore, rich mining companies were prospecting each summer for uranium. At Baker Lake the Eskimos hired a lawyer to stop the government from granting permits to prospect. The game was being frightened away. And now that very same material the white man hungered to take out of the earth was going to kill them all. Why were they in such a rush to die?

The villagers appreciated the general's soothing words of consolation. He told them there would be no harm and no one would suffer from radioactivity. But Thornycroft didn't understand the Chipewyan mentality. Once before they had heard the government spokesman talk about the arsenic poisoning which came from the gold mines. Some of their own folk near Yellowknife had become sick from that poison.

Thornycroft was dutifully doing his job, but he didn't satisfy Florence Catholique. She knew a dozen trappers who went hunting with their families and lived with them for weeks at a time in the wilderness. Some hunters had actually reported seeing fragments but had the good sense to leave them alone. Who could warn trappers who had no radios and saw no newspapers? Who could warn the animals upon which their livelihood depended? Also, there had been strange signs recently. A stray wolf had wandered into the community of Snowdrift. No one knew why. He loped through the village, leisurely, without fear. No one had ever seen anything like this before. The wolf stopped and sat on his haunches and howled until someone shot him dead. Also, two dogs had died and no one knew why. Perhaps they had been sick and would have died regardless of what happened elsewhere. The Indians were Christians and should not believe signs; Florence Catholique admitted that. Maybe they meant nothing but to simple people in times of stress every new sign is significant.

Captain Caesar Jordaens, the Canadian Forces officer, accompanied Thornycroft and spoke after him. With diagrams and simple terms he tried to explain to the Chipewyans exactly what radiation meant. He experienced some difficulty with his audience; they sat stony-faced throughout the lecture. The story that the splinters from the satellite were poisonous was not entirely true, he said. The metal and dust were radioactive, but it would take a few days for someone to become sick if he took the pieces home. No one enlightened the Indians on the various degrees of radiation. They must stay away from all pieces of strange metal they saw on the ground and report them at once to the closest RMCP constable. There was excitement at the meeting when someone suddenly recalled that four trappers with their families were living at Artillery Lake. A member of the tribe must warn them immediately: they could be close to some of the debris. Noel Drybones was nominated to warn the families and he would leave soon to tell them of the danger.

There were many questions and Thornycroft took several hours to answer them correctly. He didn't have too many of the answers but he showed a genuine concern. The general realized that few of the fears of the Chipewyans were appeased and he would be incapable of doing more than he had. Perhaps the cities that had narrowly escaped Cosmos should have been rejoicing that the poison from the sky had come down upon a distant and remote land where the first settlers had predated the white man by thousands of years. Perhaps Thornycroft might have been tempted to think that it would have been better if the cities had endured the pestilence and left the Chipewyans free. After all, the white man had made the poison against which there was little cure, and he made it out of the rocks which abounded through the land of the Chipewyans. And a white man had now brought the message. The paradox was enough to confound anyone.

When Thornycroft left Snowdrift late that night, he was not satisfied. He was aware that he had only told part of the truth. He knew as little as anyone else did. The Chipewyans were closer to the truth than he was.

15

All through February, Richard Wagner kept shuttling back and forth between California and Edmonton. This was a critical month, in which many important decisions were made, and as US scientific advisor to Operation Morning Light, Wagner played a central role. It was by good luck that I was able to get an interview with him on one of his trips back to Livermore. He was there only for a short time, with a quick stop in Washington planned before his return to Edmonton.

Wagner adapted himself well to the drastic climatic change between Canada and California. If he was under strain he showed no sign of it. Nor did the complexity of the problems he had to face seem to disturb him. He did not even complain about having to leave the glorious warmth of California. But Wagner is never a man to be dominated by emotion when he is engaged in work. This would scarcely be advantageous in the laboratory that developed many of the most deadly nuclear weapons in the world. Wagner has been intimately connected with all the military research at Livermore.

Jeffrey Garberson, the public relations man who normally chaperones Wagner when he meets the public, joined us for the interview. A tall, engaging man with a good sense of humor, he shows a great willingness to answer questions truthfully and at great length. Garberson had not been up to Edmonton: he heard the news from his colleague Dave Jackson and as a result felt slightly left out of things. But he believed firmly that one spokesman in Canada would be enough. He is more like Wagner than like the high-powered Jackson: his tones are soft and he keeps the pressure low. Wagner's conversational manner is as mild as the breezes that ruffle the palm trees outside his office.

Wagner entered the interviewing room where Garberson and I awaited him. He was very much the scientist, administrator, high executive – obviously in a hurry, but trying hard not to show it. He did not wish to appear impolite. Wagner is a man with a mission. In his head he keeps the major secrets of the United States nuclear program. As he sat down he launched without delay into the program that is being pursued by the Americans in Canada. In doing so he explained one of the functions of NEST.

"Suppose, for example, that a stockpile in Europe was overrun, or a nuclear weapon stolen in the United States. We have to be ready." Wagner was concerned, it appeared, with how NEST would respond if nuclear weapons fell into the hands of dangerous and unauthorized individuals. Perhaps he was thinking about this before he came into the room. But he dropped the subject as suddenly as he took it up and went on to talk about Operation Morning Light.

Cosmos, Wagner explained, had given NEST new scope and dimension. It had been immensely rewarding and would surely result in improvements in NEST techniques, equipment, and resources. When I reminded him that for the Canadians Operation Morning Light was more than a military exercise, he looked a little disturbed at the intrusion, then touched briefly upon the case of the Athena missile launched in July 1970 by the US Air Force from Green River, Utah. The missile went out of control and landed in Mexico instead of the White Sands missile range for which it was programed. It was found three days later in the desert at Tinneon, Mexico by the Aerial Radiological Measuring System (ARMS) which preceded the formation of NEST.

The radioactive cobalt sources were eventually cleared and most of the fragments retrieved. But the Athena missile search was of minor proportions compared to Morning Light. No one mentioned that a Mexican peasant picked up a piece of radioactive metal from the missile and took it home. It killed him and his entire family.

Cosmos is a very matter-of-fact operation, according to

Wagner: "You go in on various levels and clean up." Nothing more. His is a cold clinical approach. There is no use wasting time. You get the job done quickly with minimal inconvenience. One senses that, below the hard pragmatism, Wagner is a compassionate man if he only had the means and occasion to articulate his feelings. But they are deep below the surface, submerged by his training and devotion to efficiency. It would be difficult to function effectively at his level with too much sentiment and still produce the results he has. Wagner is high enough up in the scientific hierarchy now to warrant a printed biographical handout. But this does not disclose much of the man. He is the most authoritative scientific personality on the NEST team. More than anyone else he embodies the qualities of the men associated closely with all aspects of nuclear development.

Wagner's own responses are best expressed in figures and diagrams. On the rare occasions when he discusses the human element, he does so in terms of his familiar "trade-off" of a human fear against the results of a scientific benefit. There is no waste in his sparse, contained personality, either in words or emotion. He is reticent and modest in his demeanor, but this is more of a desire to be factual, to extract the essence of every situation. And if one continues to extract only the essence there is left at the end a sterility, barrenness.

Facts roll off Wagner's tongue with ease. His "trade-off" also involves himself. In a way he is always measuring causes against effects. He speaks from a great reservoir of information compiled during his career in the nuclear business. That the words "radiation" and "nuclear exposure" strike a certain terror in people scarcely seems of relevance. That is frivolous for a man operating at his level. And yet you cannot call Wagner insensitive. His manners are civilized, pleasant, hospitable, considerate. He really wonders what all the Cosmos fuss is about. This type of accident is part of Wagner's "trade-off" psychology, a risk you take if you wish to make progress in research. And what applies to Wagner applies to the remainder of NEST. From the top, he sets the style.

In reply to a question about Costa Kruger's observation

Wagner explained in his evenly modulated voice that the orbital speed of Cosmos was seven miles a second. When it was slowed by the atmosphere its velocity was only a few hundred feet a second. This was not fast enough to penetrate three feet of solid ice. Therefore, you could throw out Kruger's theory about the satellite core making a huge hole in one of the lakes. You listen with a certain amount of fascination to the man. One looks constantly for a flaw in his smooth, superbly integrated delivery. There has to be one somewhere. But where?

I reminded Wagner of Paul Mudra relating his own experience on the ice between Baker Lake and Yellowknife. In the middle of winter he saw flowing patches of water on the rivers and lakes. This means there were areas of thin patches of ice. Wagner dismissed the idea that the core could have gone through one of these thin patches. There are scientific explanations, he insisted, that prove the core may not have survived the reentry.

Wagner checked his watch. He had about another ten minutes before he must leave to catch his flight. But ten minutes with Wagner can be most informative. One can gather insight into an organization in which ideas are not too frequently aired with the public. Perhaps Wagner would like nothing better than to be left alone. But who can leave alone a man who carries around such secrets?

In summing up, Wagner talked about the benefits of Operation Morning Light to mankind. The term might sound pompous but there is no other apt description. It is mankind, after all, who is riddled by fear. And it is the young who are most concerned. The ignorance of people about deadly radiation is due largely to the reticence of Wagner and his colleagues to talk more. But how does a person break that reticence with the FBI and CIA overseeing in the background?

"I see two benefits from Cosmos," he said. He suggested that one might postulate a third, but didn't elaborate. Time was still hurrying him. "I think it's too early to make a full appraisal." He was gathering his thoughts quickly. "We will first of all have cleaned up a modest hazard with radioactive material."

"Modest hazard?" I asked.

"It depends," he qualified. "If you find a pretty hot piece where people are living it's serious. If you don't find any hot pieces where people are living it turns out to be a negligible hazard. We're still in the process of assessing it."

Then he said casually, almost forgetfully, "My impression is that there is a region of hundreds of square miles in the area of Snowdrift in which there are hundreds of small items. Tiny specimens. The area is very large and if some of the source is there it may turn out to be hotter than we have found so far. Then I would say the problem is larger and it's going to take longer and US involvement will take longer."

I asked Wagner again to consider the social problems caused by Cosmos. He pondered the question, but social culpability for nuclear destructiveness is an obsolete thought among the new breed. It has been phased out. The question can only be misunderstood.

"It's a risk-benefit trade-off. If the benefits of using nuclear power for satellites or whatever other activity are high enough to operate a risk, then sure, you go ahead and do it. That's a judgment awfully difficult to qualify. There's one end of the spectrum that says I don't want to accept any additional risk no matter what the pay off is."

Maybe there is some inner turmoil. If there is, the alert, expressionless exterior hides it well.

Wagner was an attractive character as he dashed out ahead of Jeffrey Garberson. He was right, as it would turn out: the problem was of greater magnitude than anyone thought at the time. As I watched him leave, I suddenly remembered that he had only told me one of the benefits from Cosmos. The first was that "a modest hazard" had been cleaned up. I wondered what the others might be.

16

Outside the military hanger at Yellowknife Airport the weather is poor at 8:00 AM on this dull, chilly February morning. A heavy mist obscures the far end of the runway and visibility has closed in to 100 feet. Captain Dave Smith decides to wait around before beginning the day's search flight. He wants to see whether the weather will clear. His yellow Otter is still warm and comfortable in the heated hangar from where it will be wheeled out into the cold just before takeoff. This hangar is the one that doubles as a decontamination center for the returning teams of Cosmos searchers. At the far end tapes are still in position on the cement floor where a special area is cordoned off to check everyone returning from a field trip.

In the glass-walled mezzanine overlooking the Otters in the hangar, the pilots are waiting for the latest weather reports from Reliance and Snowdrift. Major Bob Levia sits with them, drinking coffee. He expects to go north to Inuvik, about 800 miles away at the Arctic Circle, on a routine flight. But his trip also looks doubtful: the weather is clearing too slowly to fly to the isolated Eskimo settlement, the northernmost outpost of the army. The journey has to be done in daylight, which in February does not last long here. But the days are slowly lengthening so that by June there will be hardly any darkness.

Lieutenant Colonel Butchart suddenly comes in wrapped up in his parka to check on the weather conditions. He shakes his head, dissatisfied with the fog. It is drifting off too slowly, and is still so low that the stunted trees at the end of the runway can't be seen.

"It looks like we'll have to call it off," he says. Butchart is most reluctant to do so. He is working to a close schedule and is under pressure from Garland to clean up all the located debris as soon as possible. Just then the phone rings and Butchart quickly answers. It is the weather station at Fort Reliance. The fog is clearing and the depression moving off eastward. As if by magic, the sky suddenly lightens and some of the trees once shrouded in the woolly clouds around the airport are clearly outlined. But Butchart is a careful man. He doesn't like to take chances. He tells a story about a small plane that crashed when it tried to bank at too slow a speed. There doesn't appear to be any relevance to the story, but the pilots listen politely and make no comment. They know they will have to make the decision themselves whether or not to go. Levia's son enters, takes the keys for his father's car and disappears. Don Libby, Smith's co-pilot, is working out the course to Fort Reliance, between leisurely puffs from his cigarette holder. Butchart looks out the window again, shakes his head sadly and recalls that he has forgotten to mention one important item. If the Otter leaves it will also have to carry the crew from the disabled Chinook left two days ago at Reliance. The crew will have to service the helicopter so it can be flown back to Yellowknife for overhaul. It is badly missed in the search operations. Then, with another quick glance at the thinning fog, Butchart departs, leaving the pilots to wait for the weather to resolve the issue.

At about 9:30 Smith instructs the ground crew to wheel out the Twin Otter on the tarmac. He is going. The Otter will only be flying at 500 feet or less and the weather has lifted sufficiently to the east to risk the journey. Up north toward Inuvik conditions are not good and Levia will have to wait.

Then the phone rings and Smith answers. Another unexpected complication has arisen which threatens to create a small crisis. Diachuck's Chinook helicopter cannot lift off the ground. Butchart reappears from the stairs and informs Smith that Pat Cahill and Ross Brown will have to be transferred from the disabled Chinook to the Otter since they will be responsible for picking up the radioactive particles on the lake near the village of Snowdrift.

This, for me, is now a personal crisis. Burt Meek from the

153

Fort Reliance meteorological station and I have the lowest priority and one or both of us will have to remain behind. Otherwise the passengers, spare parts for the Chinook and drums to contain the debris will overload the plane. At the last moment the flight sergeant from the grounded Chinook at Fort Reliance, with gentlemanly tact, says that his presence is not really required and he can miss the trip. We all march down to the plane now standing on the runway. But it still looks as if the Twin Otter has one person too many and Butchart takes a quick glance in my direction. I do my best to ignore the meaning-ful stare: I do not intend to be heaved. The elegant Libby solves the crisis admirably as he stubs out the cigarette in his holder. Smith has worked out the weights on a slip of paper and shown them to his co-pilot. Libby tells Butchart he is taking everyone. The harried Cahill and Brown show up a few minutes later by truck from the disabled Chinook. Their heavy steel drums, to be used for the debris, are securely strapped in the rear of the Otter.

Smith has already started up the two motors. He is anxious to begin the journey so we can return in the low ceiling while there is still enough light. There are few navigational aids on the Barrens and the pilots fly by dead reckoning with the map on their laps, referring constantly to the terrain. It won't be too difficult to do this today since we fly first to the extreme eastern end of Great Slave Lake, land at Fort Reliance and then double back west to Snowdrift.

The yellow-bodied Twin Otter has RESCUE emblazoned on either side in large letters. It can carry nineteen passengers or a load of 12,500 pounds. Within a hundred yards and with a full load she lifts beautifully into the cold misty air. Smith turns slightly to the north and then east, less than 500 feet above ground and 100 feet above the tops of the small pines that cluster on the side of the hills. Within minutes the last wooden houses of Yellowknife are behind. Off to one side I can see the garish yellow building of Sigvaldason's newspaper near the lake in the old section of the town. Then in a few minutes there are no more buildings, only the Barrens below.

The Otter is churning smoothly toward its destination. All

eight seats are taken and the flight engineer is huddled in his small collapsible canvas chair near the door. He engages occasionally in conversation with the pilot through the intercom. The noise of the motors is so loud we cannot converse intelligently without it. Guenette, the veteran French Canadian from the downed Chinook, reads the comics. Ross Brown has fallen asleep.

The mist dissolves and the sun appears as the plane lifts over a high escarpment on the edge of McLeod Bay on the eastern extremity of Great Slave Lake. The plane is well heated and reasonably comfortable, even though everyone is dressed in heavy arctic clothing. After about an hour one can see a few dark spots on the snow beside the lake and the disabled Chinook with its drooping blades. The hard-packed surface of the snow looks very clean and sparkles brightly in the sun. The air is luminous in the pure, sharp light. There are some empty fuel barrels on the lake near the helicopter. Libby takes the Otter in just above them and lands easily on the aluminum skis which are fitted over the wheels. The plane slides to a halt and then the throttle is opened wide for a second or two so the skis move over the snow. Smith repeats this maneuver several times. There is a trick to landing with aluminum skis on the snow in the north. Friction on the aluminum causes great heat; if the plane stops for more than a few seconds while the skis are hot, ice forms and glues the Otter solidly to the ground.

Everything is fine. Guenette and his crew step down carrying spare parts; Burt Meek from the weather station follows them. There are twenty-seven people at Fort Reliance but no one is out on the lake in the crisp cold morning to greet us. Smith doesn't wait for more than a few minutes. He wants to take the two AECB men and their containers back to Snowdrift and complete the mission. It is noon but the sun is still low in the sky. It will not rise higher and soon will begin to sink into the west.

A few minutes later the yellow Otter is under full throttle, gliding over the snow for take-off. In seconds the pilot has lifted the plane into the sky. The propellers seem to shatter the bright air throwing off splinters of sunlight.

The village of Snowdrift consists of no more than thirty small wooden houses, some hardly bigger than enlarged shacks. The pilots locate the army tent and the colored bunting on this eastern end of Great Slave Lake. Once more an easy landing is accomplished. The motors are throttled up again, the aluminum skis ease forward several times and then the pilot cuts off. Smith and Libby, not wishing to go through the decontamination procedures on return to Yellowknife, stay in the cockpit, but open the window in the streaming sun. In the warmth of the sun you are not conscious of the $-20°$ temperature. You almost feel the heat beating down on your face. You disregard the weather. In the distance the huskies howl and thin corkscrews of smoke spiral above the chimneys of the houses in Snowdrift.

The Twin Otter is met by three soldiers who have waited by their insulated arctic tent erected on a small mound in a grove of trees. Once the Otter's motors have stopped, the soldiers come out on the lake to greet the plane, swearing joyously: they are glad to have some company. They offer coffee brewed over the primus stove. It cools quickly.

These soldiers have been searching the lake for radioactive Cosmos particles and have discovered a number of new locations. There is nothing very big on the snow. The pieces are only micromillimeter in size and are buried below the surface. But some, surprisingly, register as high as one roentgen at contact. Corporal David Lovejoy, who heads the small detachment, has been here for two nights and will remain by the lake until the radioactive particles have all been removed. But no one is yet aware of the widespread contamination on the lake. That news will come later.

Charbonneau and de Laurier, the other two soldiers, have brewed up fresh coffee. Constable Bill Liechtmeijer of the RCMP makes his appearance as part of the welcoming party. He has been sent here to keep the Chipewyan Indians at Snowdrift away from the Cosmos debris scattered on the lake. The Chipewyans are naturally very curious about all this unusual attention suddenly being paid to them. Since General Thornycroft's visit the usually peaceful lake has become a hive of activity. Otters land and take off, sometimes several times a day. Whirling helicopters hop over the countryside. The final blow delivered to their privacy has been the invasion by the peculiar men from NAST wearing yellow suits and carrying their counters. One thing the Chipewyans had always had was their peace and isolation. Now that, too, is gone. But the RCMP constable is the law. The Chipewyans listen to Liechtmeijer and believe what he says. It has always been that way in the far north.

Without warning the constable leaves us and jumps aboard his red snowmobile and roars away over the snow to head off another similar vehicle coming from the village. About a mile away the two meet in the middle of the empty white isolation of the lake. A short conversation follows and a minute later the intruder turns around and heads back to Snowdrift. Liecht-meijer explains when he returns that one of the Indians had come to investigate a marked-out area and he had to explain that no one must approach the pieces of metal buried in the snow.

Cahill has dragged the heavy metal drums out of the Otter and placed one on the Mountie's skidoo. He will go with the constable to the more distant section of the bay, shovel the particles into the drum, then bring the drum back to the Otter. Meanwhile, I tramp over the snow with Brown, who is checking the hit zones to see how far the radioactive particles were dispersed. Once, when Brown stops near the soldiers' encampment in the grove of trees, the detector jumps up. It looks for a moment as if the camp is sitting on top of a hot piece of debris, but the reading doesn't repeat and Brown goes back onto the lake again, sinking to his knees through the thin crust.

The entire afternoon passes locating the particles and then shoveling them into the drums. It becomes evident that there is a good deal of radioactive material on the lake which the Hercules cruising down the microwave ranging system grids have missed. The encamped soldiers with their detectors have been regularly coming across more debris.

It is growing late and the pilots, who have sat watching the activity disinterestedly through the open cockpit window and drinking hot coffee, are becoming impatient. When the sun dips behind the hills a wind begins to whistle over the open ground like high, piercing notes on a flute. The temperature drops rapidly. A little wind in winter has a vicious effect in the Barrens.

The loaded drums are heaved aboard, lashed down at the rear away from any of the passengers. Then Smith turns over the motors. A few minutes later we wave goodbye to the soldiers and to the lone RCMP constable standing a distance away by their tent. They had already put the hoods of the parkas over their woolen hats. Clouds of moisture crystallize in the air as they shout farewell. The Otter taxies onto a smooth patch of snow, lunges across the surface at full throttle and rises into the west.

The balding, moustached Smith flies at low level, a few hundred feet over the trees, toward Yellowknife. One quickly develops a great respect for these Otter pilots. Next day, Smith would be off with Bob Levia to the far Eskimo settlement at Inuvik. Beyond Inuvik is the Beaufort Sea and the Arctic Ocean. It is a frozen route of ice, forsaken by time, where a forced landing would be disastrous.

I watch some caribou loping across one of the lakes. The snow is deep, and sometimes the animals sink through the crust up to their bellies; with a great effort they pull themselves free and trot on over hard ground. Their hoofs make delicate punctures on the sparkling white depression. With the sun vanishing deep in the distant hills, the first houses of Yellowknife appear; moments later we come in view of the runway as the Otter gains height and circles over the town. A few minutes after that the plane descends into the swiftly settling gloom as the lights of Yellowknife flicker on to greet us.

17

When the Twin Hueys and Chinooks finally return from their numerous investigations on the lakes and hills, twilight has settled over Yellowknife. The night is cold and crisp, the air almost brittle. Footsteps on the dry, hard snow make a sound like crunching glass. The clouds of smoke seem suspended forever above the chimneys of the wooden houses. The yellow clapboard sidings of Sigvaldason's *Yellowknifer* are brilliantly bright in the clear moonlight. The ravens are still making lazy circles above the garbage dumps on the edge of town.

Across the ice of Yellowknife Bay, lights from the shanties in the Indian village of Detah glow dully. At the airport's military hangar the last of the helicopters flutter down like clumsy, noisy birds flapping their wings in time to the powerful beat of the engines. The rotor blades suddenly stop and the men clamber down carrying their instruments and computer tapes, clumsy in the padded nylon boots and heavy arctic suits, mufflers and woolen hats. As they remove their ear plugs a brown army van is waiting with its engine running. The last of the group pass through the NAST decontamination control on the hangar floor. When they are declared clean they climb into the bus and ride the five miles into town to the Northern Command Headquarters.

The road is as blank and uninhabited as the Barrens. A hundred yards off it you could lose yourself in the wilderness. Lieutenant Colonel Butchart and his second-in-command Major Harris are busier than any time they can remember since they joined the army. They are doing their best to coordinate the thousands of activities of Morning Light from Northern Command headquarters.

Most of the scientists and technicians in the buses sit quietly; they are hungry and thoughtful: sporadically they discuss the success or failures of the mission. The technique has become routine but each search is different: each presents new conditions, new problems. The weather is never the same and the excitement of the country is such a powerful stimulant that the men grow animated as they recall the day's activities. By the time they see Butchart and give their reports they will have forgotten about their fatigue. Some of the men, like Cahill and Brown, have snowshoed from the landed helicopters through the bush checking the sites with detectors. Sometimes they relocate the hits registered from the helicopter and sometimes they don't. The radiation is easier to find from the air than from the ground. Unless they hover right over the site and drop a marker they can miss the tiny area where the hit was originally made. It is heavy work for the men of NEST who stumble and struggle through the deep, crusty snow. None of them except Joe Tinney and Benny Lopez have ever been out before in such cold.

On this particular day, Ross Brown lost his pants and Pat Cahill had to have the lapels of his parka cut off when they were found to have been exposed to radioactivity. The Canadian NAST men detected the contamination in the routine nightly check. Ross and Cahill are the men most likely to risk contamination on the search. They perform as an experienced team. Their hours of work have been as long as anyone's and they have the additional task of not only flying all day in the helicopter but of disembarking in the bush and snowshoeing through deep snow to find and remove the Cosmos debris.

Cahill looks forward to relaxing with a beer at the hotel after reporting to operational headquarters. This is his nightly routine. A veteran of World War II, he seems to have limitless energy. Brown, on the other hand, suffers from earlier fatigue. He dozes off on the plane between destinations. Tonight he desires nothing more than to rest after the day's work.

In the warm, friendly operations room, the men strip off their bulky outer garments and place their gamma ray and infrared equipment neatly on the table. Benny Lopez wears a red and white scarf that reaches down to his feet. The scientists and pilots take hot coffee from the dispenser and drink it thankfully. There is a confusion of voices – a number of discussions going on at once, involved technical talk about the interpretation of the results.

Kirk Knighton, the photographer from EG&G, places his camera lovingly back into the gleaming steel box that holds all his equipment. Knighton is security-conscious, very suspicious of strangers looking over his shoulder. But he is not home in the US, where he could call the security guards or the FBI. This is Yellowknife. The only security guard is the uniformed woman at the entrance who doubles as the switchboard operator.

Some of Knighton's shutters didn't work today. They refused to function in the freezing temperatures. And this had not even been one of the most chilling days: the temperature had risen to $-20°$.

Brown and Cahill are engaged in a discussion with Butchart. They want to make absolutely sure there will be more drums to house the radioactive debris. A number of hits recorded on Great Slave Lake near Snowdrift had to be neglected because there was no place to store the material. They must go back and finish the job. Richard Lynn is walking nervously up and down the room with a long sheet of graph paper in his hand, trying to interpret the read-out on the chart from the gamma ray spectrometer. With his free hand he removes his outer garments.

On the telephone Butchart is talking to Colonel Garland, his commanding officer in Namao. Butchart urgently has to prepare for the new campsite to be built immediately at Lake Cosmos, in the Thelon Game Sanctuary about 350 miles east of Yellowknife. The army engineers figure they can safely use the lake runway at the new camp until mid-March. After that, if the search continues, they will have to think of something else.

In one corner of the operation room Lieutenant Glen Diachuk, Lieutenant Wayne Krause and Captain William Sorfleet are quietly sipping coffee. For these helicopter pilots, as for everyone else, it is the termination of a fifteen-hour day. The next will begin tomorrow morning at 7:00 AM when they meet the army bus in front of the Explorer Hotel.

Instead of the day's activity dying in somnolence it has revived amazingly. Malcolm Brown, the Sergeant Quartermaster, is a very practical man. He now appears on the scene to look after the requirements of the searchers. He produces everything from a can of soup to a small spring needed to repair some equipment belonging to NEST. He has the facility for finding the right item at the right time – night or day. He is on twenty-four-hour call – and usually someone calls him every few hours.

There is a slight distraction. Some of the men are discussing the exploits of the famous Japanese explorer and adventurer Naomi Uemura. Two years ago Uemura skied down the glacier face of Mount Everest. He fell and slid for several miles and came to a stop before a crevice. He has arrived in Yellowknife accompanied by a team of Nippon TV cameramen. From here he will fly to Greenland, where he will learn from the Eskimos how to control a large team of sled dogs. Then, in three weeks, Uemura will set off alone on the 3,000-mile journey from Thule to the North Pole. The Smithsonian Institution in Washington has arranged to monitor the brave Japanese's journey through a specially built transmitter that will give an automatic reading of his position to a satellite.

The world will not know of Uemura's success for several months. But as daring as his venture may be, he departs in the shadow of the satellite. For he cannot eclipse Cosmos. Uemura is racing against time. His survival will depend on beating the spring breakup of the Arctic Ocean on his return journey. He will be traveling through the ice age valleys of Greenland that have never been properly mapped, valleys eternally in the grip of glaciers. The land is more forsaken than the Barrens. Morning Light has given the men a small taste of one of Uemura's objectives, "to challenge the limit of human endurance." The expedition excites the admiration of those who discuss it. But the conversation soon changes.

Sorfleet is examining the maps around Resolute and

Snowdrift with some of the NEST men. Russell Lease and
Joseph Tinney are trying with difficulty to retrace the route
along which they made several hits. Sorfleet has an uncanny
knack for putting his finger on the exact locations. This is much
more difficult than one can imagine in a land where there is a
terrifying similarity between every outcropping of rock and
where one lake looks almost exactly like any other. Not all the
helicopter pilots have this facility. Sorfleet is quick, nervous,
alert and exacting. He has a command of the details and a clear
uncluttered mind. One wonders what brought this kind of man
into the peacetime army. He explains that his father was a permanent soldier before him. He is thin with a sensitive angular
face and short army regulation hair. Garland is very strict about
hair discipline. There is an army barber in residence ready to
enforce the rules.

Krause is outgoing, gregarious and talkative. He may be as
good a pilot as Sorfleet but one might feel more confident with
Sorfleet in charge. Krause is a big, grinning good-natured man
with a thick moustache and a squarish, large, kindly face that
suggest the physical features of his German ancestry. Diachuk
is smaller and quieter. He listens more than he talks. Like all his
comrades he is a dedicated professional. Defense Minister
Barnett Danson thinks these men are the finest helicopter
pilots in the world. They are certainly operating in some of the
most rugged terrain. A few days ago they were flying in a 30-knot
wind at $-40°$ with a wind-chill factor that made it about $-70°$.
Winter is no time to make a forced landing.

The flight engineers like Mike Guenette are usually older
men with fifteen to twenty-five years' service and have the
rank of sergeant. The engineers know every inch of the aircraft
they fly. One of the Chinooks is out of action at Fort Reliance
and will have to have a battery replaced. They have been flying
all day and sometimes in the night. Something in one of the
machines has to give way. The air crews have the same zeal and
dedication as the scientists. Altogether, the atmosphere is one
of enthusiasm. Butchart hardly issues an order: his commands
are more like discussions. The men respond quickly and in-

stinctively in the confident, fraternal mood that prevails in the operational command headquarters.

Sorfleet's helicopter has found five pieces of debris in three days in zones one and two, which are in the area immediately east of Yellowknife. The Hercules aircraft have been fairly accurate in flying down the close guidelines and reporting any areas where there is radioactivity. The helicopters will investigate these hits, searching the same region with less sophisticated detection equipment. Using the microwave ranging system, which has allowed the Hercules to fly their patterns with amazing accuracy, the spectrometers have registered almost too many hits for the helicopters to investigate and evaluate with their hand-held instruments. But Sorfleet's experience has been that there is always something to be found in a region where the Hercules reports a hit. The pieces of debris Sorfleet recovers are frequently in locations close by but different from the ones reported from the big planes. This leads him to speculate that there may be a good deal more debris about than anyone realizes. The radioactive material buried in the snow emits such an irregular pattern of radiation that Sorfleet's helicopter has to overfly the area several times before making contact. It's slow patient work. But Sorfleet says he is looking for "the pot of gold": the uranium core. He won't be satisfied until he finds it.

One of the small pieces of Cosmos which Sorfleet's group accidentally came across registered 100 roentgens at a few feet. Others registered about 30 roentgens. If you remained close to any of these for any length of time you could get a harmful dose of radiation. Locations were marked with the usual orange bunting, and at the same moment Yellowknife was notified of the hit by radio. The code words Oscar, Lima, Sierra, Foxtrot indicate a significant find. Call sign Charlie signifies a high level of radioactivity. The discovery the day before of the 100 roentgen fragment was dangerous and call sign Charlie went out. Instruction for the pickup of that piece would have to come from Namao in several days, when the new 200-pound lead drums were ready and there were sufficient hits in the area to make it worthwhile to return. Logistics were always important in these pickups. The aircraft had sufficient fuel to cruise about part of the day, land on the snow and then cart off the containers to Yellowknife where the Hercules flew south with them. In the confined space of the Twin Hueys, prolonged exposure to the containers might not be such a good idea. There was always the possibility of contamination. The containers were less of a hazard in the back of the Twin Otters, or in the spacious storage compartments of the large Chinooks.

Sorfleet takes some delight in explaining the difficulties. The work for him is almost endless. As he talks the voice of Lieutenant Colonel Butchart rises high in the background on the telephone. He is having logistics problems again with fuel. Butchart has only twenty-five barrels of fuel remaining in the local dump to supply the downed Chinook at Reliance. The helicopter cannot have more than ten barrels until a decent fuel supply is built up. The discussion with Namao goes on. Fuel consumption has become a real problem for the aircraft that fly extra long hours. Service problems for the technicians and supply organization are infinite.

Sorfleet, as a practical man in the field, finds, like everyone else, that the system of detection is imperfect. New hits are located in old areas declared clean. Hits are discovered in places where they are not supposed to be, though when the higher-flying Hercules discovers a patch of man-made radiation Sorfleet knows there will definitely be debris somewhere in the vicinity. How much he cannot tell; nor can anyone else. The process of recovery is like straining through finer and finer filters for the radioactivity. The final filter is the ground team who land with the helicopter and go on to the snow with hand-held counters. Often debris can't be seen but has to be shoveled together with snow or ice into the drums. It will be a great find for Sorfleet if he can discover his pot of gold. But he is beginning to believe it doesn't exist. The scientists who accompany him are doubtful, suspicious of the scattered fragments that are more widespread than they believed possible. They will not yet draw any positive conclusions – they want empirical evidence. But the writing is already on the wall.

"We're running into all sorts of problems," Sorfleet says. "Cold weather problems. The maps up here are very poor. Since two governments are providing people there tends to be more discussion than decision-making and there don't appear to be experts in the field who know everything. So you get an expert on the microwave ranging system, an expert on uranium. Americans detect the radiation and the Canadians pick it up. Then you have the aircraft captains who are physically flying out there. There are so many things that everybody wants. You're limited by space and fuel. And you try to keep everyone happy and still try to accomplish something worthwhile." Sorfleet's keen young mind is grappling with problems he has not come up against before and he is confused. It is also eleven o'clock at night. He has been up since 6:30 AM and the night is not over. His report for the day is still not compiled.

"There have been great delays," he says, "and certainly the military has not been innocent. Parts have arrived slowly. We ran out of fuel today." He stops to talk to Butchart.

Sorfleet and the other pilots have been lucky. So far there have been no accidents. This is only due to the special safety precautions the pilots have been ordered to take. Everyone is aware of the difficult conditions under which they operate.

"Things are going very slowly. It will take months. Everybody is very safety-conscious. And nobody wants to insult any of the other people in the organization. The Americans think something can be done very quickly and they tell the Canadians. The Canadian man on the scene has to go back to his superior and say, 'Look, this is what we figure should be done.' Decisions seem to be made on a very high level. It takes up a lot of time." Sorfleet shakes his head resignedly. In the end the helicopter had to find just a square yard of snow that maybe they would pass over half a dozen times before their detectors responded. It was slow, debilitating work. It would never be finished. Sorfleet suddenly reminds himself he has not eaten all day and sends out for some Kentucky Fried Chicken on Yellowknife's one main street.

18

In the evening, when their day's work is done, the scientists, the technicians and some of the helicopter pilots usually gather for dinner in the dining room of the Explorer Hotel. Sigvaldason would no doubt be happy to witness the truth of his pronouncement that the Cosmos searchers have brought a winter prosperity to Yellowknife. The Explorer has never done such good business in the off season. It charges as much for a room as the Sherry Netherland in New York, the George V in Paris or the Dorchester in London – and you carry your own bags. The owners might deny this but there is a little exploitation taking place. Cosmos has transformed the character of the hotel. The owners know a good thing cannot last forever. In the hotel shop, an enterprising businessman has increased his order of colored T-shirts that display the black Yellowknife raven astride Cosmos. The raven hasn't changed his expression. He still says, "What, me worry?" At Lawrence Livermore, Bell and Morrison will proudly wear these as proof of their sojourn to distant Yellowknife.

At a large table in the dimly-lit dining room almost the entire cast of NEST is present. One wall is nearly all glassed so you can see the moonlight lying on the snow and the small pines sloping away over the hills. At the table are Dick Lynn, Benny Lopez, Russell Lease, Bill Ayres, the photographer Kirk Knighton, Joseph Tinney and Charlie Prevo. They are joined by the helicopter pilots Diachuk and Krause. Those who are not here are in Namao at Garland's operational headquarters.

The scientists are as exact about their food as they are about their work. Lynn is very concerned with his salad dressing and with the vegetables that accompany the large Yellowknife steaks.

Prevo, a physicist from EG&G, has just joined the group and Lopez has gone over the instruments with him all day to acquaint the newcomer with some of the modifications. Prevo has a large domed forehead and wears rimless glasses. Having only arrived from California, he finds the environment distinctly strange. He has an involuntary nervous twitch about his mouth which causes some distraction. In a day he will be working out in the field with his colleagues.

Joseph Tinney is anxious to return to command head-quarters with Lynn after dinner to work out a problem concerning one of the computers. He says he needs a clear head and refuses even one glass of wine. Instead, like some of the other NEST members, he prefers to drink milk. Tinney is one of the more interesting members of the team. He feels there is some-thing almost spiritually significant about his visit to Yellow-knife. Ten years to the day before Tinney was alerted for Operation Morning Light he left for Greenland to participate in Project Crested Ice. He finds the coincidence very odd. At Lawrence Livermore Tinney is head of NURE, the National Uranium Resources Evaluation. Before that he headed Hazards Control. His PhD is in nuclear engineering and he has won many awards in the academic community. He possesses one of the keenest, sharpest and most determined minds in the group.

Once Tinney sinks his teeth into a problem he can't let go. We are discussing the case with which, I suggest, anyone who has a knowledge of physics can build a do-it-yourself atomic bomb. The information seems readily available to anyone who looks for it. The conclusion one draws is that there are no secrets in the world which can be kept. Tinney rejects the proposition vigorously but, in doing so, explains how a bomb can be built and why it would be so difficult even if you were capable. Knighton, the photographer, always hypersensitive to the credentials of strangers, listens in amazement. He thinks I am out to steal the secret of the bomb. But I'm not recording Tinney, I'm merely impressed by his wide command of the subject, his unusual memory and seemingly Boy Scout purity. He is also quite conventional, athletic, adolescently youthful and a fine soccer player. In common with many of his comrades he has the capacity to isolate himself exclusively with his work. The environment is extraneous to his needs. All he requires is the machine.

Tinney finishes his milk, excuses himself with Lynn and dons his parka against the cold. The command headquarters is only a few hundred yards down the hill, at the bottom of the road. The fact that Tinney has been up since early morning, out all day on the helicopters, is irrelevant. He has irrepressible energy for his work, a peculiar restless desire to solve all problems large or small.

The other men continue to eat with deliberate care, unconcerned by the departure of their friends. When the blond Ayres finishes his dinner and drinks his beer, he takes out a plug of tobacco from his pocket, breaks off a piece and begins to chew. I have never seen a tobacco-chewing physicist before. Like Lease, he is a hunter and a fisherman and hopes he will have an opportunity to make use of his talent for both in the north. Lease, the biologist from DOE, is divorced and unattached. He is in no great hurry to return to the sickening fumes and crowds of the big city. He would like a chance to fish the graylings that abound in the lakes and reach a weight of forty pounds. The hell with Morning Light. Lease wonders how he can prolong his stay in this grand country. With or without Cosmos it has been well worth the experience for Lease, who is integrating himself well with the locals and feels at home as the DOE representative in Yellowknife. His immediate boss in Canada is the deputy manager of NEVOO, Troy Wade. The head man Mahlon Gates is away in Washington but will be back soon. Lease blends unnoticed with the bar dwellers of Yellowknife who come up to the Explorer for a night out.

Krause, the helicopter pilot, is lounging against the small bar at the entrance to the hotel. He has had several whiskies and is feeling happy and indifferent. In the morning he will be cold sober and able to fly without any trouble. Tomorrow is Saturday, and Saturday night is a big night for the young of Yellowknife. It is a night when the pilots rent hotel rooms, buy a few bottles, invite up some women and have a good time. There is a woman on the staff of the army magazine *Sentinel* whom Krause has his eye on. Yet bold as he is with his Chinook helicopter, he appears to be bashful with women.

The waitress behind the counter is leafing through a copy of *Time* magazine. On the cover is a picture of the United States CIA Chief Stansfield Turner. Hovering to one side of him is a caricature of a Soviet spy satellite. As the girl reads it, the cover with the satellite faces the slightly drunk Krause, who pays no attention.

Benny Lopez is always grinning even when he's serious. He has thick black hair, rather long by Canadian Forces standard. Krause makes good-natured fun about Lopez's hair. "What is a Californian-Mexican doing in Yellowknife?" he asks. Lopez may be a Californian-Mexican but he was up in Thule in winter on Project Crested Ice ten years ago with Tinney; Greenland is just as cold as the Barrens and as empty of people. But Lopez is not a man to disclose facts, especially about himself and what he does for a living. He laughs his nervous little laugh and makes no comment to each humorous jibe by the pilot. Krause invites Lopez to a drink and he accepts.

Sitting by himself at a table draining the last of a glass of beer is the AECB man Pat Cahill. His fellow worker Brown, a generation younger, is sleeping the sleep of the dead in his room. As their chief Roger Eaton says, they are protecting Canadian sovereignty by personally putting each piece of Cosmos into a Canadian black plastic garbage bag and shipping it back to the Whiteshell Laboratory. It is difficult to know whose sovereignty is really being protected. No doubt the United States personnel would like to get their hands on the debris and take it back to their own DOE laboratories. But the Canadians jealously guard this precious radioactive metal. And Cahill, as the man in the field, oversees its dispatch to Whiteshell. So far Cahill has carted off about twenty-five pounds of material from a satellite that weighed about five tons. Most of the machine is still missing. If the core did weigh 100 pounds, not more than 1 percent of the enriched uranium 235 has been found, most of it in microsized particles, congealed from a molten state into small solid pellets.

Cahill is a paternal, bulky figure, older than the United States NEST personnel and double or more the age of the pilots who fly him. But age makes no difference here. He puts in a long, wearisome day, longer in many cases than his colleagues. On the site he protects his canisters of deadly fragments with zealous care, warning others to beware. His pencil-sized dosimeter is always with him and he will take it out at unexpected moments and hold it up to the light. Satisfied that all is well, he will shake it and return it to his pocket. Pretty soon Cahill grows tired of talking to the young pilot about how large DOE's budget is compared to the AECB's. He finishes his beer. Then the older man pays his bill and goes upstairs to the room he shares with Ross Brown.

The NEST team have dined well and have left their table. Lopez puts on his brown parka and wraps his long woolen multi-colored schoolboy scarf around his neck. He is returning to the operations room to check the gamma ray equipment for tomorrow. Prevo, the new man from EG&G, trudges uncomfortably after him in ill-fitting Arctic clothing that has only recently been issued from the stores at Namao. As they leave, the locals are filling up the tables of the dining room, which becomes a tavern in the evening. The NEST men and pilots dissolve into the darkness beyond the subdued light spilling from the huge window. The countryside looks all blue from the light. In the morning, very early in the new day, the men and machines will begin their careful work again, searching for more debris along the footprint.

Part Three

CONTAMINATION

19

Roger Eaton is a tallish, conservative man with considerable gray hair brushed down over a large, wide forehead. Eaton has a sense of importance about him. Sometimes that sense of importance conveys a pompous air that is probably not intentional.

The AECB is what its name implies: a control agency for atomic energy in Canada. It has a small staff and a relatively small budget when compared to its gigantic American counterpart, the DOE. In polite recognition of Canadian sovereignty and pride the DOE defers decisions, if at times somewhat impatiently, to the AECB. They have responsibility for recovering and disposing of all the debris of Cosmos. But out in the Barrens in sub-zero weather, instructions are not always followed to the letter. In practice, Cahill, Brown and other AECB searchers are frequently helped in their work by their American colleagues.

Eaton arrived in Edmonton on January 26 and soon after became the scientific spokesman for Morning Light. Some people objected to this. They did not find the AECB spokesman altogether to their liking, or this quasi-independent government organization sufficiently forthcoming or open. The AECB had become a law unto itself and liked people to know it was in command. On the other hand, Dave Jackson didn't accept the idea that his boys from the DOE should take a second place to anyone. And this attitude was probably justified, considering the massive US effort expended in Morning Light. Although Jackson may have embarked on his public relations duties in the spirit of a holy crusade, on the whole the Canadians didn't object too much to the role of the public relations man from Nevada. Below Colonel Garland, who indisputably controlled Morning Light, lesser celebrities jostled for position. Wagner

controlled the US scientific community, but he was not asser-
tive. He knew his strength.

Eaton saw himself as the arbitrator, the man whose job it
was not to be a scientist but to define the problem. He had all
the cliches of the trade at his command when he referred to
"crisis management" or "gut feelings." But he would not rush
into a room and say, "We have just found seven more goodies,"
the way Jackson did. By no wild stretch of the imagination could
Eaton conceive of radioactive debris as "goodies."

Eaton was most insistent that "Canadians had to make their
own judgment," and "there could be no recovery of debris
without Canadians for reasons of sovereignty." This issue
reappeared frequently. For a nation like Canada suffering from
the agony of two traditions threatening to split the country, this
is an issue best left alone. Eaton was not the only scientist acting
as if a foreign nation had invaded the private scientific sanctum
of Canada. The generous assistance of a neighbor who had
come to help was not always appreciated. But in spite of the
Canadian belief that they could have done the job alone, this
was an exaggeration of their resources.

"My job was to force clarification of the problem – to keep
things moving, and they did move," Eaton later said.

One hardly needed to keep things moving in the Yellowknife
area. They leapt quickly ahead on their own momentum in the
highly volatile situation. In his discussion one was hoping Eaton
would talk more about the dangers of Cosmos. And he eventually did, but he warmed slowly. He is not a man to open up and
speak freely. Even so, it was obvious that Eaton was as troubled
as anyone else by the threat to Canada's north. Small or large,
the area of danger was extending tens of thousands of square
miles to the west and south of the original footprint.

From mid-February the expanding menace of untold numbers of small particles flung by the wind or showered to earth by
the reactor core of Cosmos had been discussed on many occasions. No one was sure whether this was bad news or good. At
least part of the whereabouts of the core could now be accounted
for, but it was still a very small percentage, perhaps less than 10

percent. What happened to the other 90 percent or more? There were mysteries to solve. Government spokesmen, especially elected ones, do not like to leave mysteries with the public. They breed uncertainties, fear, suspicions. A definitive statement, even if it's wrong, sounds better than an admission of ignorance. There was no policy. The Department of National Defense passed out terse reports through Colonel Jean Boulet, the public relations chief in Ottawa. At Livermore one was referred back to Whiteshell for the facts that related to chemical analysis. For anyone seriously interested in the facts, the bureaucratic carousel provided nothing but frustration and delay.

Eaton explained that the by-products of the fission process created in reactors such as those in Cosmos are strontium 90, caesium and cerium. All are lethal if radiation doses are high, or if sustained in low doses over long periods. Strontium 90 can be deposited in the bones; particles of uranium fission products are soluble in stomach acids. They can be ingested by caribou and humans. It was Eaton who issued the warning to the Indians not to eat the bones of the animals they hunted.

Eaton would become peeved when asked questions about Canada's relationships with the uncooperative Russians. He would formally request that all such questions be referred to External Affairs. This deference was disturbing. The policy of open information, stated early and frequently by the Minister of Defense, did not seem to apply to the AECB. Here the curtain was being drawn. The issue deserved to be in the public domain no matter how much the scientists and authorities wished to downgrade it. If in a democracy there is a public fear, whether groundless or true, that fear deserves to be aired, not hidden.

The men from Livermore who invented Polaris, Poseidon, the Multiple Independently Targetable Reentry Vehicles (MIRVs) and designed the neutron bomb were at Yellowknife and Namao. Their presence, however innocent, somehow added a new and awesome dimension to Operation Morning Light.

Every statement of importance was qualified all the way down the line. But Eaton expanded a thesis which did make sense. The machine weighed about five tons. By the end of

March the searchers accumulated 100 pounds of material, a fraction of which is the uranium core. A good deal of the uranium may still be up in the atmosphere, but this theory is discounted. Eaton estimates Cosmos had a three-minute burn-up period as it entered the atmosphere. A good deal of uranium could turn to dust or float away with the wind during those few minutes. Maybe. But everyone was puzzled. When scientists of the Hit Evaluation Panel would meet in Garland's operations room and speculate on the subject, there were as many theories as answers. The meetings would usually settle for one conclusion and, like a Cabinet decision, there would have to be unanimity. One face would be presented to the public. "But the core just can't disappear," Eaton said. Some of it oxidized in the atmosphere. Part vaporized, liquefied. The microgram-sized particles that are almost invisible to the human eye have come down almost everywhere in the new zones west and south of Yellowknife. Some particles are caught up forever in the troposphere and will orbit the earth like tiny satellites.

But there had been some disconcerting happenings. At Fort Smith, some 250 miles south of Yellowknife, a soldier making a random test picked up a radioactive particle. This was no major hazard – yet who would care to ingest it? The wind had whipped the radioactive debris disturbingly far south of the footprint. Where else had it been strewn by the elements? Will the snow and rain be radioactive? Had a kind of metastasis spread the disease over the whole body of the north? Where had the uranium gone?

Eaton answered questions like these cautiously: "How much is spread over the ground in a very large area we just don't know. We can't come up with enough pounds of uranium. I don't know." When asked once more about the true nature of the satellite he added, "You may consider that as information we don't want to give out."

On February 21 the Twin Huey helicopters had concentrated their detection operations in three main areas: Snowdrift, Fort Reliance and Cosmos Lake. Then the helicopters continued south and west of these communities, according to the

Department of Defense statement, to "determine the extent of the small radioactive particles dispersed south of the satellite trajectory. These particles range from buckshot to pepper grain in size. Similar missions were flown on 22nd of February to the north and east of Fort Smith."

And again, as early as February 23 and 24, two Twin Hueys "were further able to define the area of low-level contamination caused by small particle dispersion at the western end of the search area. Approximate boundaries were established on the north, east and south sides. The northern boundary runs from Fort Reliance to a point thirty miles north of Fort Smith. The southern boundary is an east-west line to an as yet undefined western boundary. The helicopters were still attempting unsuccessfully to establish the western boundary on 24th February." This communiqué put out by the Department of Defense passed practically unnoticed. What it meant was that the original footprint had been enlarged by tens of thousands of square miles. The minute particles that Cahill and Brown once landed on the ice to pick up with such diligence are being ignored. The official statement continued: "No radioactive contamination has been found in Fort Smith." A week later a radioactive particle was discovered there by accident when a soldier checked his hand-held detector. But this was considered a coincidence. A stray particle of micromilligram size can be blown by the wind for many hundreds, indeed thousands of miles. And the detectors are hypersensitive. They will pick up radioactivity from a marble floor or kitchen utensil.

By March 3 the AECB and Ministry of Health and Welfare of Canada felt sufficiently confident that "in their opinion people living in the area where the satellite debris fell should not be concerned about changing their life style or recreation activities." Numerous reassuring statements were made and later contradicted. The evidence of contamination grew more rather than less confusing as spring approached. The assessment of the danger was being made constantly by United States scientists from the Department of Energy and Canadian scientists from the Geological Survey and the AECB. Militarily sensitive material that might cause undue concern to the population was deleted from press releases.

In April, particles of enriched uranium that formed part of Cosmos' core were uncovered hundreds of miles from Yellowknife, as far west as Buffalo Lake and Hay River. New deposits were found in the townsites of Snowdrift, Pine Point and Fort Resolution. The Chipewyans of Snowdrift were once told there was no contamination in their village. But no longer. "Measurements have shown," said the official report, that "the particles will not have added significantly to the natural background radiation. Nevertheless, to avoid possible health risks from close contamination and ingestion of particles in water melted from snow, it was agreed that clean up activities would be conducted in the townsites." The report also observed that "Particles have not been distributed in a dense pattern but are scattered randomly and quite far apart. For example, in Snowdrift six particles were found roughly 200 feet apart. Thus cleanup in towns, or wherever crowds of people are expected to congregate, is perfectly feasible."

Soon geological survey teams were going to go out into the north and continue with their routine geological summer surveys for uranium. There was something immensely ironical about man now having to compete with nature to find what belonged to whom. But the scientists were only concerned with the practical consequences. They were not given to philosophical introspection on the subject of radiation. The empirical facts dominated every issue. In March, Richard Wagner and some of his colleagues went up hurriedly to Namao again to reappraise the situation. They were the people most experienced in atmospheric fallout, having measured it carefully when they exploded their own nuclear devices. They knew the characteristics.

The ultimate fate of Cosmos was still an uncertainty. But the scientists liked tidy explanations for public consumption. Was there a pattern of behavior that could be established? Many people were guessing; no one cared, any longer, to be quoted. With increasing frequency particles were being located in the eastern search regions. At Fort Resolution the NAST team went in to clean up an undisclosed, unknown number. A section of the Fort Resolution airport runway was contaminated. In a small Indian village twenty miles northeast of the town a few small pieces of debris were discovered. Officially it was stated that forty-seven sources were recovered in all, but this was all that registered.

A NAST team flown into Pine Point in early March admitted they could only complete "five percent of the cleanup." A survey of the local high school revealed "a boot found with contamination." Sick and dead dogs were now routinely to be checked by band councilors in the remote Indian villages. At Hay River a total of twenty-nine hits were registered by mid-March, but this was probably a small group out of the many that it was possible to find. A new cluster of hits near Snowdrift registered by a spectrometer aboard a Hercules could not be relocated.

By the end of March there were too many possible sources for the men and equipment to handle. It was becoming an epidemic. On April 3 it was announced that "forty fishing lodges have been searched and cleared." The best that could be done by the time spring breakup drew near was to take a given area known to have considerable contamination, evaluate the density of the contamination and apply the rule to a similar territory. It began to look as if that rule could be applied to over 15,000 square miles.

Another official report in spring stated categorically that "coverage of the area east of Cosmos Lake is now complete." This meant zones four to eight, which included Baker Lake, were clean of debris. The authorities were taking a very optimistic view of their capabilities. Their pronouncements would prevail until by chance a stray Eskimo or Indian one day stumbles across a piece of Cosmos debris. The behavior of the powerful wind of the upper atmosphere that flung the remains of Cosmos so wilfully over the countryside was not as predictable as had been thought originally.

On March 10, a peculiar incident came to light which

demonstrated how much anxiety still existed about the core of Cosmos. At 1600 hours Mountain Standard Time, the small RCMP detachment at Cape Dorset sent a radio message to Edmonton. A twenty-five-year-old Eskimo out hunting seals had suddenly braked his dog team of huskies to a halt, turning over his sled in the excitement. Before him yawned an eighteen-foot crater in the lake ice. The ice was at least five feet thick and big chunks of it were flung hundreds of feet away like toy blocks. Some of the chunks were over eighteen inches in diameter. The RCMP gave the position of the crater as exactly twenty-five miles northwest of Cape Dorset, and told local residents to keep well clear of the site.

All the north was extremely sensitive to the possible danger of radioactivity since the arrival of Cosmos. Cape Dorset is 1,500 miles from Yellowknife, north of Hudson Bay on the southwest corner of Baffin Island. It was a long way from the footprint. If the Barrens was a land scarcely inhabited by man, Cape Dorset was beyond the outer rim of civilization. Ice and snow remained twelve months a year.

Three days after the discovery, on March 13, a Twin Huey helicopter was disassembled, placed on board a Hercules and flown to the nearest airfield to the crater – 250 miles east, on the island at Frobisher Bay. Meanwhile a special team from the Canadian Forces, AECB and Lawrence Livermore Laboratories were airlifted by an RCMP Twin Otter to Cape Dorset. Here the scientists boarded a snowmobile and rode the remaining distance to the site on the unnamed lake to investigate the phenomenon.

In this silent land of snow the crater and the scattered chunks of ice were an impressive sight. A nervousness existed about any crater whose origins could not be immediately explained. Probes into the water produced no radioactivity and on the lake bottom an underwater camera revealed no debris. But the constant seepage of water and the construction of the crater that disfigured the smooth contours of the lake surface deeply concerned the scientists, the RCMP and the Eskimos who claimed they had never seen anything like this before. The Eskimos said the crater could be, at the most, a month old. A thirteen-man encampment installed itself at the site to continue investigations. Shortly afterwards, a Canadian government scientist, Doctor Frederking, who specializes in water resources, was flown to Cape Dorset after the investigators confessed they could make no definitive statement.

Frederking, after a day of taking ice samples, probing into the lake and carefully inspecting the adjacent ground, came to his conclusion. It was a natural happening – some kind of ice boil built up by the mounting pressure of the ice pack itself. Under these conditions the ice would rise to a head, then collapse into a crater with an explosion of fragmenting chunks. The explanation was as odd as the weird event, but no other theory could be advanced. The Eskimos and RCMP had their reservations about this explanation. They knew the north. Something mysterious and unexplainable had occurred. This was an incident about which the shaman of the Eskimo, who once guarded their religious heritage, would have felt uncomfortable. The strange crater would be a subject of conversation for years to come among the Eskimos, woven, as all important stories are, into their colorful folklore.

Meanwhile, activity continued elsewhere. South of the Great Slave Lake, ten sites were selected and samples of the snow taken from each. All the samples were sent to Whiteshell to be analyzed so the ratio of active particle distribution could be determined. Water reservoirs and intake filters were carefully scrutinized at every settlement in the eastern zones, and at any other place that requested assistance. The NAST became a common sight among the small northern Indian villages, but their presence did not give the Indians much confidence in the government statements that all was well everywhere in the Northwest Territories.

At around the end of March, the weather in the Northwest Territories grows milder. And the mild weather brought with it a slowdown in the search activities. The reason for this slowdown was simple: it was not so much a termination of the operation as a beginning of a new phase, the realization that valuable men and expensive machines whose services are very much in demand elsewhere could not be spared any more. NEST had given its best for much longer than it contemplated. Its members were needed back in their own laboratories for essential research. The Canadians would continue throughout the summer. Instead of the cold to contend with there would be the sweltering heat, the plagues of mosquitoes and black flies, the quagmires of muskeg, the paddling of canoes and portaging around the torrential rapids.

Although the search techniques were modified, Cosmos was still out there on the Barrens. It lay like some malignant evil, sucking from man his resources and strength. It was a kind of phantom who mocked the searchers' ingenuity and managed to elude them even to the end.

The number of men who crowded into Colonel Garland's operations room dropped dramatically after March. Meetings that used to be attended by twenty-five now attracted five or less, and of these, most were Canadians from the Geological Survey. Only a single US advisor stayed on. The last microwave ranging system flight took place on April 15. The helicopters still went out on close ground searches but soon they would stop as well. After that it would be the turn of the summer teams to commence their work. Camp Garland on Cosmos Lake, which had been the center of operations, had been disbanded at the end of March. The lake ice was cracking from the weight of the 78,000-pound Hercules.

The NEST team back home at their laboratories were beginning to turn their minds to other problems. But all the telephone lines were open between the various laboratories in the US and Ottawa. There was still a considerable amount of outstanding business. And there was one man in particular who felt there were important decisions yet to be made.

20

Canada's Geological Survey has its offices in the outskirts of Ottawa, away from the busy center of this civil service town. Most locals have never heard of the Geological Survey. Others, civil servants, vaguely know that it is connected with the Department of Energy, Mines and Resources. Even employees who work close by are themselves unfamiliar with its exact function.

The corridors of the Survey are filled with gaudily-colored maps illustrating the country's vast mineral wealth, much of which lies beneath the surface of the Northwest Territories. Along the corridor, in one of the small, nearly identical offices, Robert Grasty spends most of his days when he is in Ottawa. Grasty, a tall, angular, reflective man whose short goatee is tinged with gray, has the quick movements of a person in constant agitation. In conversation his mind tends to drift off to any problem that might be troubling him. When I went to see him in May, 1978, Cosmos was preeminent among these. His frugally decorated room was littered with graphs, maps and data accumulated over the preceding three months. Grasty had been so intensely involved with Operation Morning Light that he seemed to live with it day and night. It absorbed him, dominated him, exhausted him.

Grasty was responsible for operating and interpreting the results of the Canadian gamma ray spectrometer for fourteen hours a day on the Hercules. Like the other scientists he attended all the briefing meetings, offered contentious advice and sometimes advanced unorthodox ideas which did not always meet with a cordial reception. After six days of this, dropping from exhaustion, Grasty was sent home to Ottawa to recover; he then went right back again to Edmonton. Altogether, by mid-April he had been up to the Yellowknife area on five different occasions. And he was still not through. He estimated that he had at least a year's work ahead of him. Grasty probably spent more time flying up and down the Cosmos footprint than any other scientist, and he will be going back again and again until he has finished his reports and satisfied himself that his conclusions are correct. Sometimes he muses that there may never be a conclusive report on what he has uncovered.

Back in 1964, when Grasty took his PhD in paleomagnetism in the peaceful grounds of Cambridge University, he hardly dreamed that he would ever find himself in the midst of such soulsearching turmoil. He is a restless, inquiring man driven by a consuming wish to make known his findings. He wanted the helicopters at Yellowknife to keep flying at a low level over Great Slave Lake so his surveys can be completed. But he knew this is impossible. The army, after three months, had to redirect its resources elsewhere. But his own work would continue: he would speak to Livermore, the AECB, the Department of National Defense, anyone who will help him finish his job. His understanding chief, Arthur Darnley, a competent scientist himself, realized the importance of Grasty's findings and considerately gave him his freedom. Darnley is a good man for an inquiring scientist to work under.

Grasty reaffirms that he has more material on the reactor core than anyone else. "I know I have. I've done a complete systematic survey." He was probably right. No one anywhere had given such a single-minded devotion to the mystery of Cosmos' lost reactor core.

One conclusion, he said, is now indisputable: the core did not burn up in the atmosphere as many scientists suggested. But as he said this he was already thinking ahead. His mind is constantly full of unsolved problems, uncertainties.

"Normally," he told me, "you would never fly a lake. But I knew it was contaminated very early. I had flown it many times. From flights over the lake I could tell what's on it." Then he became silent when asked how contaminated the Great Slave

Lake was. He simply shook his head and didn't answer. Grasty was not being evasive: he simply didn't know because he hadn't figured it out yet. Then he did some quick calculations while he talked and looked up at the ceiling. "I guess there would be millions of particles on the ice. I don't know how many million." When the ice melted they would all sink to the bottom of the lake, and the fish would ingest them. The buckshot-like material was in the micro-Roentgen range – very low in radioactivity. But if you put enough together in the right proportion the dose would increase.

Who would ever have the courage to raise the cry that the fish in the 350-mile-long Great Slave Lake had all become radioactive? This may never be the case but it's a possibility. The person who says it's true will have to raise his voice over the official refrain that the contamination of thousands of square miles is of too low a level to cause concern. What remains out there undiscovered on the Barrens is anyone's guess. There are as many known factors as there are unknown.

Grasty has noted mistakes in laboratory and field readings, large discrepancies between radioactivity measured on the ground and from an aircraft. He has studied the erratic behavior of internal gravity waves in the air and made a chart of the debris distribution on the lake. He has measured the size of the particles at Fort Resolution and found that they were one-fifth of a millimeter in diameter and weighed ten grams per cubic centimeter. They were visible to the naked eye. Grasty also claimed that because of the change from the less accurate Omega navigation to the microwave ranging system many highly radioactive early hits were never rediscovered. How many would fall into this category he didn't know.

In the early weeks of the search, the existence of large fields of small radioactive particles had not been considered a serious possibility. Yet no one had systematically mapped the results of the distribution over Great Slave Lake. Grasty made his own survey of the region and discovered that certain areas declared clean on early flights were incompletely searched: the spectrometer failed to record the finds on magnetic tape which could be analyzed later. Nor was he satisfied with the radioactivity readings made by others. He knew that material showing high radioactivity when analyzed at the Whiteshell Laboratories had given low readings in the field. Also, the geologist was perplexed by the amount of deadly radon gas in the air. Admittedly the quantities detected were not lethal, but the find startled Grasty when he sampled the air at low level above the lake.

Grasty had crisscrossed the lake by helicopter dozens of times. The millions of tiny particles on its surface were just visible to the human eye. Because of the background radiation Grasty couldn't determine the readings over land with the same precision as he could over the lake. But one could surmise that the satellite had sprayed some of its burned-out core to the south, dusting the countryside with its poison. How far south no one knew.

There were two types of tiny, almost perfectly round globules, each slightly different in diameter, which formed as a result of molten uranium having cooled and solidified. In Project Crested Ice, the surface of the snow splashed by the jelly-like plutonium fallout was scraped clean by bulldozers and the material dumped aboard a giant ore carrier for disposal. In the Barrens, the problem was more difficult. How does one bulldoze tens of thousands of square miles?

Grasty knows very well the distribution pattern of the contaminated area over the lake. The scientist unrolled for me his precious map which he had been preparing for weeks. On it he had drawn his distribution of the debris. The map is not a projection: Grasty made it from indisputable data and it proves his point of the immense accumulation of particles. It is impressive.

Our long discussion was terminated by the ringing of the phone. Grasty expected his wife, but instead it was a scientist from another department. For a while they discussed the peculiarity of the air waves above Great Slave Lake, a subject very much on Grasty's mind. They had something to do with the radiation in the air, but he was not sure what. The air over the lake is perfect for detecting abnormalities that could have been produced by Cosmos, as it should be free of gases emitted by decomposing uranium. It will take much careful study to determine the final results.

From his map of particle distribution Grasty will be able to estimate what part of the satellite core is there and what has not yet been accounted for. What is not on the lake must be somewhere else. Perhaps a certain portion burned out, but the remainder has to be on the Barrens – either in water or on land. And since the globular particles survived, larger pieces also might have survived. Although it is claimed that small particles are floating in the atmosphere, this theory is doubtful. Extensive U2 flights high in the atmosphere have not confirmed this.

Grasty believes what has happened on the Barrens is of such unique importance that he must dedicate a year to its study. Many inconsistencies have been accepted as truth. Grasty had been so rushed in the few weeks before I spoke with him that he had been unable to calmly sit and assemble all his valuable data. The paleogeologist, one of the first men in on the search, will probably be the last one out. Although many aspects of Morning Light bother him, Grasty is not a man to make a statement unless he checks it himself – particularly where it concerns geology.

Every so often the scientist returns in conversation to his comparison of sprinkling pepper from his giant shaker over the countryside. How and where it would settle from 100,000 feet? Grasty begins with this proposition and expands it. He is a man who stimulates the kind of controversy that should be good for his colleagues but is not always appreciated. He is not an individual who can be muzzled or subdued. One thing is certain: many more facts will suddenly appear one day about the distribution of the contamination. No one is far away from Yellowknife. We are all closer than we think.

The Barrens have been dusted with poison. But the gods were generous: some of it they dropped on a lake so that when the snow melts the debris will sink into the mud at the bottom and vanish. The scientists say it will not be sufficiently active to harm the fish. The radiation will dissipate and that will be the end. But we have heard this before and in strange, inexplicable ways seen the cumulative effects generations later. The policy at the moment is to pacify a population who were not, after all, told very much at the beginning. What has occurred on the ground surrounding the lake is formidable to consider.

When one contemplates what has happened the Barrens suddenly grow beautiful. The thought of the land enduring this permanent scar makes any portion of our shrinking earth a precious place to protect. And all this is but a mild taste of nuclear terror – as Wagner said, "A modest hazard."

Keith Richardson, who has an office just down the hall from Grasty, makes a perfect contrast to his colleague. He is subdued and relaxed, quite unlike the lively and enthusiastic Grasty, who expounds his ideas with so much conviction. Richardson's demeanor comes closer to the studied and casual confidence of the men from Las Vegas and California. Perhaps this is not a coincidence: he spent several years at NASA in Houston, where he was chosen as an astronaut for one of the moon flights. (He returned to Canada when it became apparent that he faced a long wait before being launched into space.) Even though the atmosphere of the Geological Survey bears no resemblance to Las Vegas, Livermore, or Los Alamos, Richardson has picked up some of the security consciousness of those places. A sensitive man with a slight speech hesitation, he is thoughtful and mannered – more selective in his comments than Grasty. He is always uncertain of how much he can tell a stranger.

By the middle of April, like Grasty and Bristow, Richardson had returned to his office on Booth Street. At Namao he supervised the work of his associates in the Geological Survey team. Now that the spring breakup has ended the first phase of Morning Light, Richardson has none of Grasty's missionary zeal to seek the final truth. He has had enough of Cosmos.

"We are approaching the end of phase one," he told me. "In

phase two we will have to move back to the inhabited areas to make sure everything has been picked up.''

"We didn't see much strontium but we saw some caesium in one or two samples." He also confirmed that the enriched uranium 235 is spread in fine dust over the countryside south of Yellowknife. But he said it all so casually, so matter-of-factly, that you could scarcely bother to comment.

Richardson's remarks supplement Grasty's. Contamination is spread not only over Great Slave Lake but over a wider area of the country than anyone believed. "We did a survey a few days ago concerning that material spread over the countryside and it's highly enriched uranium 235. It's still a small fraction of what's going to be there naturally." Richardson wants to step out of the Morning Light project. It's not everyone's cup of tea. He is "getting back into the uranium business again.''

Grasty is a North London boy who fought his way into Cambridge. Richardson did all his graduate and research work in the United States. He has associated for years with the aristocrats in their scientific establishments. The traditions of Grasty's and Richardson's formative scientific education are a continent apart in their social philosophy. Grasty is an indignant scientist, indignant about data that should be further explored for the benefit of world knowledge. And he intends to do something about it. He is like a dog with a bone clenched between his teeth. He will hold on to it until the end.

A few offices further away the quiet Bristow dreams of better and still more effective machines with "more bells and whistles on them" to detect radiation. And he will undoubtedly build them.

The Geological Survey team is made up of good men. But they are personalities who have developed their specialty in great depth while letting their perception elsewhere remain narrow. The day of the Renaissance man, I think, is over. He would not be very much appreciated in this community of specialists and pragmatists. But when the space age machines go wrong, these are the people we need.

Epilogue

I am trying to close the ring. I am seeking the truth in the one place where the truth surely should be. But it will be difficult to find. The road to the Whiteshell Laboratories at Pinawa has been long blocked by many obstructions.

It is late April and spring has come to the prairies. Here and there the flat brown land is drying out in the warm sun. Small patches of snow are melting and the flooded fields grow fertile to receive the grain that will soon be planted. The two-lane highway is badly potholed from the winter frost. On one side the telephone poles recede like wired crucifixes to the horizon.

I come to Whiteshell with some misgivings, not at all certain how I will be received. The men from Los Alamos, Livermore and Las Vegas have already been there before me. But I don't know what information they have taken away, if any. I arrived at Winnipeg in the morning and rented a car for the last seventy miles of my journey to Pinawa, a town specially built for the workers at Whiteshell. To help me I have only three bits of information: Whiteshell employs 800 people; it has a good-sized nuclear reactor for peaceful research; and it has done all the chemical analysis on the fragments of Cosmos. I am only interested in the last piece of information. Under controlled laboratory conditions and at their own leisure the scientists must surely have come up with some interesting results.

In a way, I suppose, this is a return to my youth. I was born on the prairies in Winnipeg, before anyone thought of a Whiteshell or dreamed of a nuclear reactor. So it is a trip home and I am filled with nostalgia and early memories. Many thoughts come to my mind as the car spins down the unending flatness. But I am a little early so I pull over to a roadside restaurant, order a coffee and think.

The man who serves me has a slight Ukranian accent and he is just sending his boy off to the county school, his lunch bag packed with sandwiches and thermos flask. The boy reminds me of my own childhood. I ask the owner directions for the last twenty miles and he tells me. No one can have any idea of what has taken place behind the walls of the research establishment. But from the beginning of this trip I have not been able to shake off the feeling that I am an embarrassment to the authorities. The circumstances under which it all began the week previously were strange and disturbing – not at all auspicious.

My first request to visit Whiteshell, made the week before I began this journey, had been rejected out of hand. In effect I was told that what went on there with Cosmos was none of my or anyone else's business. The AECB was guarding its secrets. They would conceal them until they decided otherwise. Until then I had found my way into a lot of places all over North America, and people had helped me generously. Yet here at the end of the trail, in the country I know best, I would not be able to penetrate the last barrier and finally close the ring. However, there are a number of anomalies in the Canadian bureaucracy, as there are in all governments. Whiteshell is controlled by the Atomic Energy of Canada, which is an independent government body. But the AECB is a client of Whiteshell, which is doing the research on their behalf. So I am up against a client-owner relationship in which the client is also the boss.

I decided to contact my friend high in the ministry and explain my difficulties. He understood: he would see what can be done to help and call me back in an hour. In an hour came the phone call. No problem: you can visit the nuclear establishment, speak to whomever you wish and all help will be granted. I profusely extended my thanks and was given the name and number of a man named Burge, at the Atomic Energy of Canada in Ottawa. Burge arranged for me to contact a Metro Dmytriw at Whiteshell who would introduce me to everyone who had anything to do with Cosmos. Suddenly, I was high in praise of Canadian government efficiency.

An hour later my phone rang at home. A dramatic change had occurred. If I wanted to go to Whiteshell it looked now as if it would have to be over the dead body of a Dr Gummer of AECB. Gummer would guard the debris of Cosmos with his life, if required. There are more phone calls for assistance and finally it was up to my friend high in the ministry to resolve the complicated issue. If not, there would be open warfare. My ministry friend whose word must be law had evidently been fed some confidential information in the meantime which caused him to have second thoughts. Therefore he had to demonstrate the wisdom of Solomon. I would be allowed to go to Whiteshell, but I could not talk to anyone who had worked on Cosmos. But he said, "It's a fishing expedition. If you keep your eyes open maybe you'll find what you want." I had a suspicion that I would have enough difficulty understanding what I see without trying to divine the answers to complex chemical tests I am not allowed to discuss. I have to find some humor in the situation or I wouldn't have come this far.

At the small cafe on the road to Pinawa these thoughts flit quickly across my mind. I finish my coffee and set out on the last twenty miles of the search.

Tall wooden silos and a silver water tower rise abruptly on the landscape. I cross the Winnipeg River in wild flood and in a small side creek can see a beaver dam. I admire the engineering skill and industry of the beavers that went into the intricate construction of that dam. And then suddenly, unexpectedly, I am at Whiteshell. It is a much bigger place than I anticipated. There are half a dozen large low brick buildings, colonnaded down the front. One is obviously an administration center, and another low building, with a second square steel structure set on top, must be the reactor plant. Next to it soars a thin, tubular steel pole supporting a bulbous silver water cooler for the reactor. Sun glints like splinters from the metal. There are no guards to be seen anywhere behind the meshed steel fence and the gates are wide open and unprotected. What a blissful sense of peace and security in an age of terrorists, I think. Within the reception area there are also no guards; nor would I find any near the reactor plant.

John Boulton, a chemist, is my guide. He is polite, helpful and patient, but he does not talk to me about Cosmos. If I broach the subject he carefully steers the conversation into other channels. I am given a most thorough, dutiful tour. The order has come from up high that I was to be suitably chaperoned.

I look through an electron microscope which magnifies 50,000 times a piece of lung tissue being examined for silicosis. We visit the reactor, where Boulton points out the uranium bundles of rods that power it and carefully explains the mass spectrometer that separates the various isotopes of uranium. The process sounds fascinating. But it is all invisible and there is nothing to see. I try various techniques and pose theoretical questions about cases similar to Cosmos, but Boulton is too clever. He recites other theoretical cases that redirect the conversation. My frustration is steadily mounting. Deciding finally to state my case quite openly, I make it clear that I am an ignorant layman seeking to satisfy my own curiosity, and the curiosity of others, about an important subject. The public, I declare, is entitled to know the facts. Exactly what results were obtained from the study of radioactive fragments shipped from Yellowknife to Whiteshell? I can be no more explicit. Boulton, kindly though he is, says he does not know where the material is or what has happened.

We move on to the chemical laboratories, which seem peculiarly deserted. I am looking for one man in particular who I know tested the satellite metal, but he is obviously absent. The place looks like a morgue. The doors leading off the long, linoleum-tiled corridors are locked, and Boulton opens one or two with a key. He peers in and closes them again. I inquire if there is any danger in the establishment of being contaminated from radiation since I have been into the hot cell room and through the reactor plant. He says there is none. But I am still checked four times by detectors. As I watch the remote manipulator arms operate behind their windows of leaded glass separated by a water barrier, I at least know that I can see first hand the methods used in dealing with Cosmos, although the results of the research are denied me.

Indirectly I may have obtained some useful information, but there is no use, for either one of us, in prolonging the agony. After two hours I thank my host and he is happy to see the last of me.

Back in his office of public affairs at the administration building which is only a short walk from the laboratory, Metro Dmytriw is a little sheepish about the whole affair. This is the first time in his eight years at the establishment that he has seen such secrecy being maintained. Whiteshell exists to give information from its research freely to the public, and he is bothered that this is not happening. Tucked away here in the isolated prairies he really is not too knowledgeable about Cosmos. Yet he does say that altogether Whiteshell received fourteen shipments of material from Yellowknife in eight containers. All of it underwent close analysis in the hot cells. Dmytriw, like Boulton, is polite but uninformative. I thank my host and depart in the same bright sunshine in which I arrived.

Driving along on the dull flat highway that unravels like brown tape as far as the eye can see, I am stopped by a police car for speeding. The policeman is excessively polite, as courteous as my hosts at Whiteshell. My normal resentment against police intrusion is softened by the pleasantness of our conversation. We agree in the end that if I do not contest his word the matter can be amicably settled and I will be summoned in absentia. It is a better solution than I have been able to effect at Whiteshell.

As I wait in the Winnipeg Airport lounge for the departure of my plane, suddenly I reflect on a statement made to me by an AECB official a few days before. If pieces of enriched uranium are close together in a haphazard pattern strange things can happen. If the geometry is right they can begin to violently fission, simulating a small reactor. A natural reactor in Gabon,

Africa reached criticality and fissioned for centuries. My mind roams over all sorts of possibilities. I am beginning to think like Sigvaldason of the *Yellowknifer,* to adopt a healthy mistrust of government departments. Then I decide to call up Miles Myer, the analytical chemist I looked for at Whiteshell. To my surprise he knows of my visit. He tells me his instructions were to stay out of my way. If we should meet he was "to exchange the time of day." Nothing more. Myer is not employed by the AECB so he can speak freely about his feelings without betraying the trust of the client. He considered his instructions "odious." Myer is apparently a man with a conscience and not afraid to let people know about his sentiments. "One day," he says, "I hope I can tell you everything I know." I tell Myer not to worry, most facts will become known. A vast region is contaminated: that can't be hidden. The people of Canada, above all others, have a right now to know all the information that has been obtained by the AECB. This organization should be the servant of the public if it is the custodian of the public interest. The unofficial reason given for withholding information is that compensation will not be forthcoming from the Russians if the findings are released publicly now. The Russians are as practical as Richard Wagner. If there is some kind of profitable trade they will pay. If there is not, they will be indifferent. But the so-called unofficial reason is hard to believe. Money should be irrelevant. The secrets Whiteshell keep are small compared to those which are still undiscovered on the vast Barrens. One day those secrets will be given up completely.

Meanwhile, orbiting the earth are thousands of satellites. By 1980 there will be more than 10,000. Some are designed for communications, others for weather observation; an unknown quantity can peer without our knowledge into the most inaccessible corners of our planet, televising and photographing what they see. There are also some whose purpose is aggression: these are the hunter killers of space, designed to blow the enemy's vehicle out of the sky. Among all of these numberless vehicles it is not improbable that some innocent community will again become the victim of an unplanned visit from the heavens. The next morning light may be more disastrous, more devastating than the crash of Cosmos 954 in the Barren Lands.

Glossary

The terminology of the military and scientific community is full of acronyms and abbreviations which can be completely baffling to the outsider. A number of these specialized words appear in *Operation Morning Light*. The following list should make it slightly easier for the non-specialist reader to find his or her way around some of those terms that are used most often.

AECB: Atomic Energy Control Board (Canada)
AECL: Atomic Energy of Canada, Ltd.
ARMS: Aerial Radiological Measurement System
DOE: Department of Energy (USA)
EG&G: Egerton, Grier and Germanhausen, Inc.
NAST: Nuclear Accident Search Team (Canada)
NEST: Nuclear Emergency Search Team (US)
NEVOO: Nevada Operations Office (Department of Energy, US)
NORAD: North American Air Defense (US and Canada)

Sources: Oral

Much of the information in *Operation Morning Light* came directly from interviews (made between February and April of 1978) with the people who were involved in it. They are:

Milo Bell
Quentin Bristow
Lieutenant Colonel Bill Butchart
The Honorable Barnett Danson
John Doyle
Lieutenant Glen Dyachuck
Jeffrey Garberson
Colonel David Garland
General Mahlon E. Gates
Robert Grasty
David Jackson
Lieutenant Wayne Krause
Russell Lease
Richard Lynn
Ira Morrison
Paul Mudra
Binx Remnant
Keith Richardson
Sig Sigvaldason
Captain William Sorfleet
General Kenneth Thornycroft
Joseph Tinney
Troy Wade
Richard Wagner

Sources: Written

After its crash in January, 1978, Cosmos was widely reported in the international press. To list the hundreds of news stories that appeared would be lengthy and not very informative; far more interesting are various official publications, in Canada and the United States, that bear on the subject. The following list gives the major sources of this type which I found useful in researching *Operation Morning Light*. Several major stories in the popular press are also included.

Atomic Energy of Canada, Ltd., *A Layman's Brief Guide to the Whiteshell Reactor No. 1 (WR-1)*. Publication no. 2303. Revised edition January, 1968.

.............................., *CANDU 600*. A booklet on the CANDU MWe Nuclear Power System. May, 1976.

.............................., *Twenty-Five Years of Nuclear Progress*. The annual report, including technical and financial sections, for 1976–7.

.............................., *The Whiteshell Nuclear Establishment*. A booklet on activities at the establishment. January, 1970.

Department of Energy, Mines and Resources (Canada), *The Nuclear Option for Canada : The Renewable Energy Resources*. Selected Papers ER-77-2, February, 1977.

Department of Information, Government of the Northwest Territories (Canada), *The Legislative Assembly of the Northwest Territories*. Explanatory booklet.

Department of National Defense (Canada), General Information Fact Sheets on Operation Morning Light. January–April 1978.

Department of State (US), *Establishment of the Bureau of Oceans and International Environmental and Scientific Affairs (OES).* Foreign Affairs Manual Circular, No. 687. October 8, 1974.

...................., *Establishment of the Bureau of Oceans and International Environmental and Scientific Affairs.* Press release, October 15, 1974.

...................., *State Department's New OES Bureau Completes First Step in Reorganization.* Press release, June 2, 1975.

Egerton, Grier and Germanhausen, Inc. (EG&G), *An Overview of the Aerial Radiological Measuring System (ARMS) Program.* March 1, 1975.

...................., *Focus.* A magazine for employees of the Energy Measurement Group. Issue no. 9, January–February, 1978.

...................., *EGG ink.* A publication for EG&G members and their families. Issue 2, 1977.

Energy Research and Development Administration (ERDA), *The Nevada Test Site.* A booklet prepared for the Bicentennial. January, 1976.

...................., *ERDA News Bulletin.* January, 1977.

...................., *Radiological Assistance Plan. Division of Operational Safety.* July, 1975.

...................., *ERDA Response Capability to Nuclear Threats.* Fact Sheet, May, 1977.

Hart, R.G., "Sources, Availability and Costs of Future Energy." The text of a speech given by the Vice President of

Atomic Energy of Canada, Ltd., on April 22, 1977. Published by AEC, Ltd.

.........., *Why Nuclear?* The text of a speech given to the Manitoba Electrical Association, on January 15, 1976. Published by AEC, Ltd.

Health Physics, "Locating the Lost Athena Missile in Mexico by the Aerial Radiological Measuring System (ARMS)." Vol. 23, pp.95–8, July, 1972.

Lawrence Livermore Laboratory, *Energy and Technology Review.* February, 1977.

............................., *The Lawrence Livermore Laboratory.* Explanatory booklet.

............................., *Newsline* (weekly bulletin). Issues of February and March, 1978.

Mechanics Illustrated, "A Home-Made Bomb." November, 1977.

Northern News Report—Of the North, From the North. Vol. 6, no. 30, February 2, 1978.

Page, R.D., *Canadian Power Reactor Fuel.* Booklet AECL 5609, published by AEC Ltd., March, 1976.

People, February 20, 1978.

Phillips, John Aristotle, "How I Designed the Atomic Bomb for my Physics Class." *Science Digest,* January 1977.

Time, February 6, 1978.

Pon, G.A., *Nuclear Power Reactor Safety.* Booklet AECL 5694, published by AEC Ltd., October, 1976.

University Bulletin. A publication for the staff and faculty of the University of California. Vol. 26, no. 14, January 30, 1978.

Index